READING THE WEATHER

Modern techniques for yachtsmen

READING THE WEATHER

Modern techniques for yachtsmen

Alan Watts

ADLARD COLES
8 Grafton Street, London W1

Adlard Coles
William Collins Sons & Co. Ltd
8 Grafton Street, London W1X 3LA

First published in Great Britain by
Adlard Coles Ltd 1987
Reprinted 1990

Distributed in the United States of America
by Sheridan House, Inc.

British Library Cataloguing in Publication Data

Watts, Alan
  Reading the weather.
  1. Meteorology, Maritime   2. Yachts and
  yachting
  I. Title
  551.5′0247971   QC994
ISBN 0-229-11774-0

Printed and bound in Great Britain by
Butler & Tanner Ltd, Frome, Somerset

CONTENTS

ABOUT THIS BOOK

Reading the Weather is primarily written for yachtsmen because, of all sportsmen and sportswomen, those in the sailing fraternity pit themselves against the elements more than anyone. That should not prevent anyone else who is interested in the modern weather scene from reading the book. What I have tried to do here is to acquaint the intelligent layman with much of the vast store of information that has followed the marrying of traditional forecasting techniques with the computer and the weather satellite. Some of this revolution in weather information is seen on the TV where 'paintbox' techniques allow sequences of charts, rainfall predictions, etc. to be delivered in a short – too short – weathercast.

The airwaves are full of weather charts and information. Fluxing through your room (or wherever you are) as you read this are all the weather maps you could want – and many you would not want. These are being broadcast across the world by radio facsimile, and all you need is the equipment to receive them. The fact that the vast majority of readers will not have such facilities at their disposal is because the cost

of fax machines is still much too high. But that could change. If you feel you need something badly enough – if you think the device could save your life one day – then you will fork out for it and hang the expense. I believe that once people realise what they are missing they will want to get and interpret their own weather charts, and then maybe before the millennium is out most sea-going yachts will have a fax machine.

However, that day is not yet here and anyway you have to be able to read the messages in the bare charts. Therefore *Reading the Weather* sets out to show you how to do it yourself by using an idea I have used myself for years – what I have called the crossed-winds rules. In chapters 6 and 7 we see that the method works by using actual surface and upper-air charts, but you do not need charts to use it. What you do need to do is lift your eyes off the horizon into the sky and think in three dimensions.

One of the primary messages I have tried to get over here is that the surface weather is largely the result of interactions with winds way above our heads. The modern, remarkable, revolution in forecasting has shown that this is indeed so because the computers have been fed with information from a successively larger number of height decks and each time their predictions are better and more akin to what actually happens. The magic of a six-day forecast that actually allows you to plan that far ahead with a fair chance of being right is in being. With fax it could be in your hands every day. Without fax you have the information in the forecasts and on the end of a telephone.

More to the point, the 12- and 24-hour forecast charts will often be correct enough for some forward tactical planning when ocean racing or cruising. It is in the prediction of isobars and hence wind strength and direction that the computer excels. It is not so much the wind as the weather that goes with it that is wrong, as the computer does not know much about that and it needs the human forecaster to clothe the isobars with fronts and troughs and say if fog will envelop a sea area or not.

Throughout this book you will find that the information has been illustrated with charts based on actual ones broadcast over the radio fax both in Europe and America. This will show you what is available to the met. services and so what information you could be asking for. In Part Two there are the explanations and definitions of weather words and phrases which will enable you to phrase your questions intelligently. Forecasters love to talk to people who have done their homework and know the shape of the current weather they are inquiring about

and can express themselves in the jargon.

I did not write this book with the intention of providing a little light bedtime reading. You will probably have to work at parts of it and use other parts for reference, but together with the tabular suggestions on possible trends and action to be found, for example, in chapter 13, I hope it will be seen as a practical book. I have been sailing all my life and I know that what you need for yachting is practical hints that will prod your basic weather knowledge and perhaps help you take the correct leg.

Weather has always been with us and always will be. It is the ways and means of interpreting the weather that may suffer change. Yet the isobaric and contour charts have been with us for decades, and so it will only be the detailed presentations that will alter in the near future. There will be better and better ways of giving the information over the TV for example, but you cannot take your TV to sea with you and hope it will always function. The way ahead for those truly interested in making sense of the weather is by picking a primrose path through the mass of professional material that they can obtain via fax. However, I hope that my book will lead people to make use of the available information through whatever medium they receive it, at the same time as looking into the 21st century with greater met. knowledge and understanding than at any time in the past so as to take full advantage of the more helpful and extensive information now available.

Alan Watts
July 1986

ACKNOWLEDGEMENTS

In writing a book on weather which contains charts, statistics etc. I am, as an ex-forecaster and one-time Instructor at the Meteorological Training School, very conscious of the debt I owe to the thousands of unsung heroes who have faithfully taken the observations which have made it possible. They have worked in all weathers, on land and sea and up mountains and in an endless succession of shifts throughout the twenty-four hours and for three hundred and sixty five days of every year. I do not forget the forecasters who analysed the charts nor all the technical people who manned the communications networks and trouble-shot the computers – one of the latter used to crew for me. Yet in the end, at the bottom of the pyramid, are the observers – people tend to ignore their contribution.

More specifically may I thank Ken Owens of Hayden Laboratories for the use of a Nagrafax facsimile printer and for the supply of charts without which I could not have written this book. Also Armand D. Bouchard of Alden Electronics for the unstinting supply of information concerning the facsimile scene in the USA.

Peter Bayliss of the Department of Electrical Engineering and Electronics, The University, Dundee, Scotland, supplied the satellite cloud studies.

The commercial forecasting firm of Noble Denton and Associates supplied charts on request.

I would like to thank the Editor of *Weather* (Royal Meteorological Society, Bracknell, Berks) for permission to use some material from back issues of that magazine, and Peter Stubbs for his help with the Stüve diagram.

Photo R.11 is reproduced with the permission of the Meteorological Office, Royal Radar Establishment, Malvern, Worcestershire.

Photo R.3 was supplied by Mariner Electronics, Admirals Court, Town Quay, Lymington, Hants.

Fig. 21.4 is reproduced with the permission of NOAA, and various other charts are based on their analyses, as is the case with redrawn charts from European facsimile stations.

Figs AR.2 and BR.2 first appeared in *Weather*, but originated from the Irish Meteorological Service.

The colour cloud pictures and the black and white studies are from the author's collection.

WEATHER NOTES

To assist in finding weather information, here are some useful addresses.

The World Meteorological Organisation produces international codes of practice which define scientifically all manner of meteorological phenomena and the ways of measuring and describing them. Their address is WMO Secretariat, Avenue Giuseppe-Molta, 1211 Geneva.

For information on American weather services contact NOAA Weather Radio, NOAA/NWS Rm 302 World Weather Building, Washington, DC 20233.

For archive material such as charts, observations, etc. but not for day-to-day enquiries: Meteorological Office Headquarters, London Rd, Bracknell, Berks (Tel: Bracknell 420242).

For marine and other weather matters of an immediate nature the firm of Noble Denton and Associates Ltd, 131 Aldersgate St, London EC1 (Tel: 01 606 4961) offer a useful alternative to the Meteorological Office.

For routine enquiries ring a Weather Centre such as the London Weather Centre, High Holborn, London WC1 (Tel: 01-836 4311). However this is a very busy weather 'shop' and you are better advised to find a local public-service station in the Telephone Book. When sailing Atlantic Europe and the Mediterranean obtain 'Weather Forecasts' from the Royal Yachting Association, Victoria Way, Woking, Surrey (Woking 5022).

Part One

1 SIGNIFICANT WEATHER

INTRODUCTION

Weather mainly consists of what falls from the skies, but can also include other factors such as fog and mist and cloudiness. First, let us point out some of the effects of weather on sailing.

Rain

Rain is wet and unpleasant but its direct effect on sailing is minimal. We do not stop sailing just because it rains. It is the meteorological reasons for the rain that give it importance. Of course if it is heavy, then temporarily, as when squally showers sweep across sea and coastline, rain does cut the visibility, but in general rain does not prevent making landfalls nor the taking of bearings, etc. on headlands, nor does it obscure lights very much. You may not be able to see quite as far in rain as you otherwise might, but sometimes you can see further as the rain tends to wash murky haze out of the sky.

It is well known that before rain the visibility is often exceptional, with the land standing out clear cut and stark against gathering rain clouds. 'When the Lizard is clear, rain is near', says a Cornish piece of weather lore, and equally when you can see the French cliffs from Dover or you can see from one side of Lake Ontario to the other, you can then expect rain.

Having suspected rain, then also expect what so often goes with it: namely the onset of lowering skies and the increase of wind that comes as a trough or a depression approaches. The rain from warm fronts starts slowly and increases more or less gradually with time. It may last four to six hours or it can be over quicker. If rain persists and winds are not strong, you are usually near the centre of a depression. Rain from fronts on the coasts that face west on to the oceans is going to be heavier and last longer than that which will be experienced further inland.

When you experience rain that is moderate, but occasionally becomes heavy, expect that the rain is due to a cold front. It is well known that the name of a front tells you what kind of air is following it. So the air behind a cold front that is passing will be cooler than now. That often means that it is cooler than the land or sea surface, which is a recipe for showers to develop. If the air is showery and on a sea track, the showers will go on day and night without much difference between them. If the showers are set off by the landmass, then they will grow by day and die out with the night. In this case the associated rain is going to make a considerable difference to sailing boats.

Showers are by definition short, sharp things that approach and pass and as they arrive they increase the wind suddenly. This increase usually comes with the rain and creates a squall that can be unpleasant while it lasts. After the rain has passed, the wind often goes much lighter before the next shower comes along.

Wind increases in almost all cases when rain begins to fall, but the increase from warm-front rain will be more or less gradual and build up to uncomfortable proportions over hours rather than minutes. There is, however, a second message to be inferred from continuous rain that appears to be due to a warm front. The second message is that warmer air follows the passage of a warm front, and warm air over cooler sea is a recipe for fog and poor visibility generally.

Many fronts that start off looking like warm fronts are in fact an amalgamation of a warm front and a cold front, i.e. occlusions. It is difficult to tell that a coming front is an occlusion until the continuous warm-front rain goes showery without any break. If that happens, fog risk is temporary because there is no warm air on the surface in an occlusion.

Rain that is thundery in nature often occurs in the summer half of the year, but while it may rain hard in one spot and not in another it is rare for much wind to accompany this kind of rainfall. Thunderstorms are a different matter as they are very big showers and produce, in some cases, massive squalls that can knock boats down if they are not prepared to meet the very strong winds that come racing out of the storms.

Drizzle

It is unwise to think of drizzle as rather fine rain. The weather conditions that go with drizzle are fraught with danger to yachts as drizzle is associated with poor visibility, low overcast skies and the ever-present risk of fog. Drizzle often comes sweeping in after the rain of a warm front has cleared through. It suddenly blots out sea marks and the land and may take some time to clear. The wind direction most associated with drizzle is around SW in Atlantic Europe and SE on the Eastern seaboard of the USA.

Snow

At the start of the season, or if you sail in the winter, snow is a possibility. It often comes in the form of snow showers in the spring, but is much more likely to be continuous in winter. Snow showers can last for a long time and so appear to be continuous. In this connection there are snowy troughs in cold airstreams that look rather like fronts as the snow lasts for an hour or more. The problem with snow is visibility. Snow cuts the visibility dramatically, and when it comes from showers the contrast with the good visibility before the shower is very marked. It can leave crews floundering especially as the cold will have a numbing effect on mind and body.

Hail

Hail is associated with heavy showers and thunderstorms. It means that the air is very cold compared with the sea or land surface. However, hail showers do not last long and therefore they are only a temporary disrupter of the visibility.

Cloudy conditions

Totally overcast skies are more rare than skies with broken clouds, and when they appear and persist, then the wind often tends to remain more or less constant as well. The exception is when the clouds ahead of a warm front build across the whole sky and we see the sun disappear into the murk. Then we expect gathering wind to go with gathering clouds.

Cloudiness by day stops the land from heating up and so prevents any local winds such as seabreezes. It has no effect on the sea. Overnight cloudiness stops the land losing heat by radiation and so inhibits nocturnal winds from blowing from land to sea. However, daytime cloudiness in summer is always being attacked from above by the heat of the sun and is more likely to show breaks later in the day. By night cloudy areas are more likely to thicken rather than disperse. Thus over the land a night forecast of cloudy conditions will mean that fog is unlikely to form and so visibility will remain generally good. Over the sea, cloud layers that are quite dry in the evening may produce rain by dawn.

Fair conditions

The term 'fair' really means a dry day with the sky between a quarter and three-quarters covered by cloud. Thus fair days allow the sun to get to the land and heat it up. So a fair day will experience the 'diurnal variation' of temperature we expect, i.e. the lowest temperature occurs around dawn and the temperature climbs to maximum in the middle of the afternoon and then falls away with evening. Fair days are usually associated with winds of Force 4 or less, but the wind may be stronger than this. As low cloud also builds with the day, in the same way a fine morning will often become fair (or even cloudy) by afternoon and then become fine again by evening.

Sunny conditions

This term means that very little cloud is expected to appear during the day and the sky will not be more than a quarter covered by what does develop. In sunny conditions we must expect the maximum effect of the land's heating to pull the wind ashore along the coast, i.e. that seabreezes will develop. Even when the full seabreeze cannot

develop because the general wind is too strong (15 knots or above), there is always a tendency for the wind near the coast to be canted in towards the land when conditions are sunny.

The inference from sunny conditions is that the area is under the influence of an anticyclone or of a ridge of high pressure although this is not always the case.

Overnight the corresponding term is 'fine', and that means that maximum cooling of the land surface can occur. This leads to a lulling of the wind over the land, to mist and fog patches by dawn and to the establishment of light off-shore winds – the so-called nocturnal winds.

Fog

This is the biggest risk to small craft outside gales, but it is much more difficult to forecast. Fog is possible whenever the air is humid and warmer than the sea surface, but it does not always occur when it is expected and sometimes it can occur even when it is not forecast. From a small-craft point of view there is fog whenever lights or land at a relatively short distance are obscured, and official definitions of it are rather meaningless. However, technically there is fog at sea when the visibility is less than a kilometre, and there is mist or haze when it is less than two kilometres.

Because the water near the coast may be cooler than that offshore, fog can occur along the coast when it does not occur offshore. Also the fact that the air has to lift up over the coastline may induce fog to form there before it forms offshore.

The only sure way to combat fog is first to obtain a radio or telephone forecast and see if fog is forecast for your sea area. If it is, then plan to make passage clear of the major shipping lanes. There is no defence for a small yacht caught in the inexorable path of a tanker when neither has seen the other because of the murk. If you plan to cross the English Channel with its vast volume of merchant shipping and there is

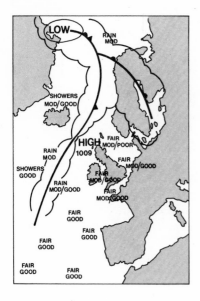

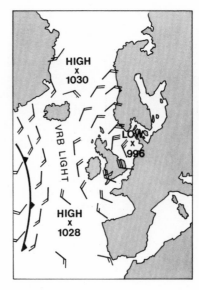

Fig. 1.1a   *A chart of significant weather as issued from the National Oceanographic Centre, Northwood, England. It is a 12-hour forecast for midday based on the chart for the previous midnight.*

Fig. 1.1b   *A North-wood surface wind forecast for three days ahead. VRB = variable.*

fog forecast for Dover, Wight and Portland, then put it off until the risk decreases. Otherwise stay inshore, but not so close as to run yourself aground.

SIGNIFICANT WEATHER CHARTS

Marine significant weather forecast charts (figs 1.1a and b) as issued by the National Oceanographic Centre at Northwood are specifically aimed at shipping in the waters of Atlantic Europe and especially Britain. They concentrate much more on forecasting wind speed and direction over the sea, and are of great help to yachtsmen who are contemplating cruising or racing offshore. Otherwise the wind speeds and directions expected over the next 24 hours can be divined from the shipping forecasts.

A typical significant weather surface prognosis for 36 hours ahead of the verification time of 1200Z as provided by Norfolk, Virginia, is shown in fig. 1.2. They expect showers and thunderstorms over the southern and mid-western states with a

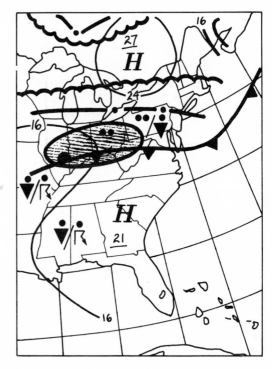

Fig. 1.2   *Surface prognosis for 36 hours ahead as broadcast by Norfolk, Virginia, radio facsimile.*

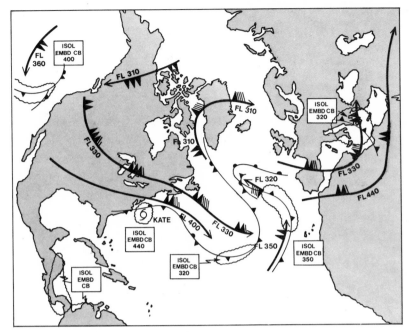

Fig. 1.3 *Significant weather chart for aviation which shows how fast the winds blow at 30 000–40 000 ft. A solid triangle means 50 kn. and a single fleche = 10 kn.*

high over the region with a central pressure of around 1021 mb. The banded zone with the rain symbol in it is an area of continuous precipitation, and to its north the dash–dot line with rain and shower symbols indicates non-continuous precipitation. North of that again, the scalloped line indicates cloudbase between 1000 and 3000 ft and visibility between 3 and 5 miles but no precipitation. We then get a clear area in the region of the high (1027 mb) before we get back into cloud and precipitation conditions.

What is or is not significant weather depends on who you are. The facsimile output is divided into stations specialising in forecasts for aviation, those that give a general coverage mainly for landlubber use and those that specialise in marine forecasts. The aviation charts for Europe and the North Atlantic are prepared mainly at the Regional Area Forecasting Centre at London Airport, and to avoid duplication of effort other stations like Offenbach 2 will take London's charts. Thus our example of a significant weather aviation chart is based on one that was broadcast by Offenbach 2,

but bore the London centre's name. The one chosen covers the height deck 25 000 to 65 000 ft and might seem to be of the most academic interest to the mariner (fig. 1.3).

However, these charts show where the jet streams are and how fast the winds are blowing. For example the jet down through the Great Lakes is rushing on at some 165 kn. (190 mph). The lows that are south of the jets are likely to develop more strongly so the remains of the hurricane Kate south of Newfoundland are a possible candidate to deepen as Kate is also associated with a front. By taking in new supplies of cold air, old hurricanes are known to rejuvenate and while not producing their tropical intensity are likely to induce very strong winds suddenly even after they have tracked all the way across the Atlantic to the shores of Britain and Europe. Any crinkle-edged 'sausages' are thick cloud layers and the legend 'ISOL EMBD CB' means isolated embedded cumulonimbus. In surface terms that means bursts of heavy rain among the more continuous rain you expect from fronts. These areas, which are potentially dangerous to aircraft because of icing and electric storm phenomena, are 'mesoscale precipitation areas (MPAs)'. See Fronts in Part Two. They are unlikely to produce thunder and lightning at the surface, although they may do so especially in the tropics.

The terms FL 330, etc. mean flight level 33 000 ft, i.e. they are the heights at which the jets or other upper air phenomena will be found in hundreds of feet. The aviation world continues to use the heights it knows and has used for years and has not yet reverted to the metric equivalents. Note that in general the height of the jet cores decreases from south to north so that the one over Africa is at 44 000 ft (over 7 Nm) while the one over the Northwest Territories is at a mere 31 000 ft (5 Nm).

Note also that the jets over the United States and the Mediterranean are accompanied by a twin further south which is blowing a little less strongly (although that is by no means always the case). These are the temperate latitude and the sub-tropical jet streams which on this day in November 1985 were close to one another. Occasionally a high-speed upper wind develops near a frontal system, as is indicated by the FL 320 jet in mid-Atlantic that is blowing from SE at 90 kn. Such isolated short jets are also usually short-lived.

What the meteorological services consider significant weather is well illustrated by an example of the chart for the 2 November broadcast by Deutscher Wetterdienst via the Offenbach fax transmitter. This was issued in the middle of the morning of 1 November for 7 a.m. the next day (fig. 1.4).

The frontal positions are important as they show where one airmass changes to another. The cold front looped down from Norway to the south coast of England and back up to Iceland is the leading edge of the first real cold plunge of air of the winter over this region. Previously the days have been relatively mild. The barring across the fronts gives a general idea that cloud is associated with these fronts and that they

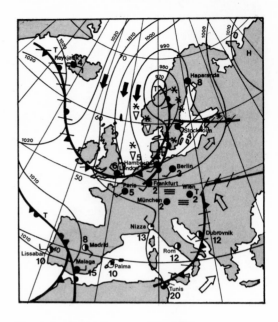

Fig. 1.4   A one-day-ahead forecast of significant weather for general use from the Frankfurt transmitter Offenbach I. T = Tiefdruckgebiet, literally 'low pressure area'. H = Hochdruckgebiet. Large figures are expected temperatures in Celsius.

are not just lines of division over which most of the cloud has dispersed. The large figures are the temperatures. So it is expected to be 5°C (41°F) over the North Sea and it will not be warmer over France and definitely colder with fog and mist in Austria and southern Germany. That coldness is due to radiation from a continental landmass at this time of year. However, 5°C over the relatively warm North Sea indicates frost inland over the British Isles, and the triangles indicate showers which will be of snow over Norway and, with snow over southern Sweden, Denmark will also be very chilly.

The black arrows show the main plunge of cold air, and the open arrows from the Sicilian Narrows up into Yugoslavia show corresponding advection of warm air there. The thunderstorms they have had in this region for some time past have now apparently died out.

The major low centre (T) is not moving much and so the snow over Scandinavia may be quite extensive. These significant weather charts are designed to suggest what is most likely, but their scale is small and so you have to use your own met. knowledge to read more into the chart than it actually portrays.

The isobars show that the strong winds are up off Norway, and in the morning winds over land will only be about 10 kn. (London) and from NW. The fully filled-in station circles over Europe show that most places will be cloudy, but that does not mean every place. Over central Spain, cloud will be broken, but the morning will be a chilly 47°F (8°C). On the French Riviera (Nizza = Nice) there is expected to be very little cloud and it should be 13°C.

These significant weather charts are the nearest one gets to a plain-language forecast over the fax and so need backing up with domestic radio and TV forecasts to put more detail on the weather for your own area.

2 PROGNOSIS

This is the technical term for forecast charts, and the 'state of the art' prognoses at the present time are the global predictions made by the giant Cyber 205 computer of the British Meteorological Office at Bracknell in Berkshire. These are forecast up to six days ahead so that the globally orientated forecasters at this World Area Forecast Centre can gain an idea of how the world's weather is shaping for the week ahead.

Once upon a time to forecast six days ahead with some degree of confidence was in most cases an impossibility, but providing not too much is expected of them and you only hope to gain the general trend of the weather, then today's computer predictions are, to those who like me left the service when the computer revolution was only in its infancy, quite magical. If you ask a weather office for the six-day forecast situation, then do not expect to be given an accurate wind speed and direction for your area over such a long span. The computer could get it right, but then it might possibly get it entirely wrong. What this kind of forecasting does is predict trends.

However, if we compare the six-day forecast chart of fig. 2.1 with the actual chart that turned up (fig. 2.2) – and I chose this example at random to see what would happen – the following wind speeds and directions are obtained.

Area	6-day	Actual
English Channel	W–NW 10 kn.	W–NW 18 kn.
Southern North Sea	W–NW 10 kn.	W–NW 20 kn.
Off East Scotland	NW 32 kn.	NW 25+ kn.
Bay of Biscay	NW 6 kn.	NW 6 kn.
Skagerrak	SW 25 kn.	W 44 kn.
Newfoundland	SW light/ variable	SW 10 kn.

As wind direction is the important element the six-day forecast gave this correctly except over the Skagerrak area. The depression off Norway was correctly forecast in position. Only its stronger circulation was not predicted. The low that the six-day forecast said would be over Greenland was in fact over Iceland but it *was* there! Having done this forecasting job as a professional I know that we would not,

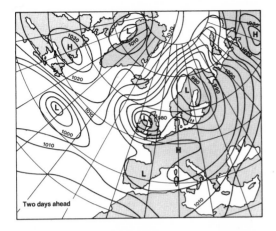

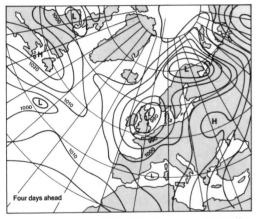

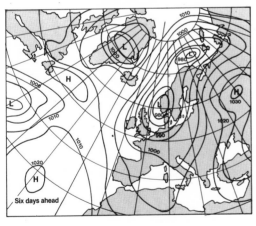

before computer-aided forecasting came along, have had the faintest idea what the chart would look like so far into the future.

Despite what I have just said, today's professionals would be the first to admit that sometimes the computer does get it quite wrong. Yet when, in the autumn of 1985, the blocking high that had settled over Britain and its surroundings sank away westwards into the Atlantic, the six-day forecast charts predicted that fairly accurately. What they could not do was to tell us that in England the night after the situation depicted in fig. 1.4 the air temperature would have fallen to values as low as −5°C or 23°F.

Coming nearer in time to the present, as well as 144 hours ahead, prognoses are made for 96 hours (four days), 72 hours

Fig. 2.2 *The actual chart for the time of the six-day forecast in fig. 2.1. It was remarkably accurate from a wind-direction point of view and not bad with respect to speed.*

Fig. 2.1 *What the week ahead has in store. Every day computer predictions for up to six days ahead are broadcast by Offenbach. Atlantic* *Europe is in the grip of a complex area of low pressure. To see what actually happened look at fig. 2.2.*

(three days), 48 hours and 24 hours ahead of the verification times (VT) of midnight and midday GMT. The whole world conforms to GMT, and so Washington's facsimile broadcasts for the early morning came to an end at 1227 GMT which is of course 0727 EST. They start up again at 1950 GMT and run on until 2350 GMT which is the end of the afternoon schedule, being only 1850 EST. Tokyo, which is 8 hours ahead of Britain, starts its overnight transmissions at 1531 GMT, which is just before midnight Tokyo time, and so on.

All this has to be because the two global times at which simultaneous soundings of the upper air are made across the world are 0000 and 1200 GMT. It is on these upper-air soundings together with the surface observations that the computers across the world work. Long and involved development of our knowledge of the interrelation of what happens above the surface with the surface pressure patterns has led to forecast charts of the upper airflow that on the whole are more accurate than the surface-pressure patterns that are divined from them.

The major pressure level with which meteorologists work above the surface is for 500 millibars (mb) or hectopascals (hPa), as in general the surface lows and highs tend to be steered by the winds at 500 mb. Also the thickness of the atmosphere between the surface and this height has been used for many, many years as a means of marrying the forecast upper air pattern to the corresponding surface pattern. Complex rules have been formulated to indicate how the thickness would persist from one day to the next and how its features could indicate the development of depressions, etc. All that has now been incorporated in the equations of atmospheric interaction on which the computers work to forecast the elements of pressure and temperature and so produce the forecast upper-air patterns. An example of the forecast 500 mb contours for the Northern

Hemisphere will be found on page 16 (fig. 3.2).

The accuracy with which the 500 mb contours can be predicted is now the same up to five days ahead as it was ten years ago for three days ahead, and the meteorologists, with their eye on the future perfect forecasting method, are always striving to get greater and greater accuracy. Their successes as they have moved from first the two-level (1000 and 500 mb) human method (a simplified version of which we will use in chapter 6) via three- and ten- and now 15-level computer models, lead them to believe that much higher accuracy can be achieved by reducing the size of the mesh of the grid of points on which the computers work.

From the yachting point of view the new computer models of the atmosphere are having singular success in predicting the explosive deepening of certain Atlantic depressions. Such lows deepen extremely rapidly and without much warning, but the computer is beginning to recognise which centres are ripe for this development. This enables far longer warning of impending gales and severe gales to be obtained. It aids the weather routing of ships and the similar routing of flights, which is of course a major preoccupation of the weather services, the spinoff from which aids the yachtsman. Such hyperactive lows are usually products of the winter months, but the summer low that deepens when it is not expected to is more potentially dangerous. For one thing more people are likely to be affected by it, and sometimes, as in the Fastnet gale of 1979, the losses of life, boats and equipment approach disaster proportions (chapter 14).

The computer models are not only formulated for hemispheres and regions. As noted earlier, they are being made from finer and finer mesh so that a 15-layer fine-mesh grid can be used to do much more detailed forecasting for a relatively small area like Britain. If you have a fax machine, you can obtain three-day forecasts of the likely areas where rain will occur and approximately how much rain is likely to fall in a 24-hour period. This information is also available either within the content of radio and TV forecasts – the presenters have seen the precipitation forecasts – or from a weather centre over the phone, or from calling personally into a weather shop or bureau. It will also aid the compilation of recorded telephone forecasts, so even if you cannot get the information first-hand it will be there second-hand. To this list of sources we must add private forecast companies such as Noble Denton in London.

3 WINDS ABOVE THE EARTH

THE ATMOSPHERE

Where the atmosphere ends as you ascend in a space capsule is problematic, but from our point of view we can say that the atmosphere stops at the tropopause. This is because the tropopause (colloquially called the 'trop') is the permanent region about 8 miles up where the temperature stops falling with height and remains constant through a great height before we enter the stratosphere. Regions where temperature stays constant with height are called isothermal layers, and the trop is the biggest isothermal layer of them all. It effectively puts an invisible lid on the weather-making processes of the troposphere below as it effectively stops air rising. It is in this way akin to an inversion nearer the surface that equally limits the height to which convection currents can ascend.

The tropopause is higher over warm airmasses and lower over cold ones. It is higher in summer than it is in winter, but from day to day it lifts and sinks, and what its actual height is can be found on tropopause charts (fig. 3.1) as broadcast by fax

stations who specially cater for the needs of military and civil aviation such as Offenbach 2 in Europe or Washington which is a World Area Forecast Centre for the American continent. The height of the trop is not of real importance to yachtsmen, who only need to recognise its general character.

The first pressure level under the tropopause which those who want to forecast their own weather should think of is the 300 mb (hPa). It is at this level that the jet streams blow, and, as in the example in fig. 4.3, if you obtain a 300 mb contour chart you will be able to see at once where the contours crowd most closely and so be able to follow the jets as they snake round the hemisphere. These high-level winds blow over the surface lows and highs which are on the move, but when a ring of contours roughly coincides with a surface ring of isobars, that means that the low or high is quasi-stationary. In the method of forecasting the future weather map outlined in chapter 6, these rings in the contours give the fulcrums of the chart – the centres around which everything else is likely to move. Further, because the 300 mb level has contours that lie around 30 000 ft, so this level is more indicative of the winds that will affect the development of the cyclonic and anticyclonic swirls below them than is the lower 500 mb chart.

For reasons that will be outlined later, the major upper level with which meteorologists work is the 500 mb. This has contours that lie around 18 000 ft, and the thickness of the layer between this level and the 1000 mb surface level is a powerful tool in unravelling the future development of surface features. However, for the yachtsman who is going to use his knowledge of the upper air to forecast his own weather, the 300 mb winds will be given to him whenever he can see cirrus cloud moving across the sky. By methods outlined in

chapter 5 he will be able to say in many instances what the wind direction is at 300 mb and to gain some idea of the wind speed. He will be able to divine how rapidly the winds are varying with height at this level, which will tell a great deal about the prospects of gales in the outlook period. With the fax charts he will be able to do much more, but the acquisition of fax is not essential to the forecast methods outlined in this book.

If the observer wants to find the direction of 500 mb winds, he will have to watch the movement of altocumulus (Ac) and altostratus (As) clouds in the middle reaches of the troposphere. Often Ac will be more helpful here, although old islands of As, left over after a front has been mainly rubbed out by air sinking from above it, can be

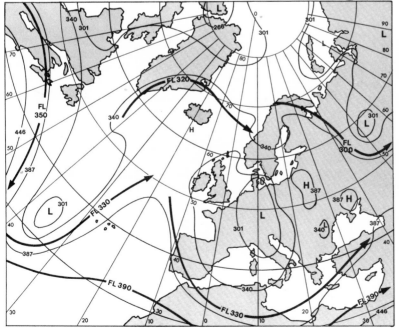

Fig. 3.1 *The height of the top of the weather is given on charts like this together with where the jet streams are blowing. The heights are in hundreds of feet (thick arrows) and the thin lines show where the tropopause is low or high.*

used as well. Recognising cloud types so as to fix their rough heights is an essential thing to be able to do.

The level of 700 mb gives the winds at around 10 000 ft and can for our purposes be ignored. The winds not far above the surface meteorologically speaking are covered by the 850 mb level, and these contours follow the winds at a mere 5000 ft or so above the surface. This is a level which may actually make contact with the surface when gusts are brought down from high above by shower clouds or thunderstorms. The winds at 850 mb ought to roughly follow the surface pressure pattern, and where they do not the general wind between 5000 ft and the surface must be reasonably light.

Finally, we come to the isobars of the surface charts. These define the run of the wind which is just clear of surface friction and which is normally assumed to be 2000 ft up. So the surface charts give the wind at 2000 ft and they complete this rundown on the standard pressure levels. The following is a résumé.

Stratosphere

TROPOPAUSE

100 mb   Something over 50 000 ft and around the height of the tropopause over the equator where it is at its highest.

200 mb   Around 40 000 ft and higher than we require so can be ignored. However, it is around the height of the tropopause in summer over the poles where it is at its lowest.

300 mb   The level around 30 000 ft which is

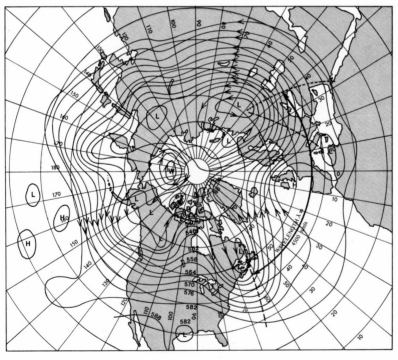

Fig. 3.2   *How the upper westerlies blew round the Northern Hemisphere on a day in November 1985. The contours form closed loops and the winds blow between them, faster where they are closer and slower where they widen out. A blocking pattern over the Atlantic has stopped the westerlies moving the weather on.*

generally above the infrastructure of depressions and travelling anti-cyclones. It is the level of cirroform clouds and is therefore the level one observes when watching temperate-latitude cirrus. In this height bracket is where aircraft trails are mainly made.

500 mb   Major upper-air pressure level. About 20 000 ft and the level of higher clouds in the 'medium' bracket. The winds at this level have the maximum effect on the development and steering of surface pressure features.

700 mb   About 10 000 ft. Level of high clouds in the 'low' bracket or low clouds in the 'medium' bracket.

850 mb   Level of big cumulus clouds which span 5000 ft.

1000 mb   Surface pressure. Low stratus, fog. Wind at 2000 ft.

SURFACE

THE UPPER WESTERLIES

When you see a contour map (see fig. 3.2) of the Northern Hemisphere (and it is the same for the Southern), the most striking thing about it is the way the contours – and hence the winds – move round in a series of immense waves.

These waves wrap themselves round areas which are low (L) and high (H). The 'low' here refers to depressions in the contours and 'high' to domes in them. Deep troughs in the waves, like the one down the eastern seaboard of North America, are indicative of the upper low there being almost immobile. Thus this part of the wave pattern in the upper westerlies has gone to sleep and will prevent the migration of anticyclonic weather into that region.

Equally the warm dome which is over Atlantic Europe is also immobile and is a block in the westerlies. It was this block that gave Atlantic Europe almost two months of anticyclonic weather through September and October in 1985. It is worth noting that the H and L symbols also mean high and low temperatures at altitude, so

we have a cold pool above the quasi-stationary low-pressure region over Labrador and a warm dome over the surface high which was centred on Ireland at this time.

When blocks occur, the normal eastward migration of the waves in the westerlies is halted and may even become retrograde, i.e. the blocks move back westwards. To achieve the latter the distance between one trough and the next must be very large. Along the 45° parallel (which is a pretty average latitude to take) and with the wind speeds prevailing, the 4500 mile wavelength of the pattern spanning the Atlantic and extending to the Caucasus is just about right to keep the wave pattern from moving. If the wind speed through the pattern should fall, the block over Britain will move back into the Atlantic, which in effect it eventually did.

The tightly bunched contours show where the jet streams blow although the 500 mb level for which fig. 3.2 is drawn is some thousands of feet below the height where the jet attains its highest speed. The contours for the jets are those at 300 mb (around 30 000 ft), but a racetrack of closely spaced contours on the lower-level chart will still show where the jet holds sway.

Other features to note are the cut-off pools and domes over the Arctic and the way the pattern weakens as soon as you get below the latitudes of Florida and the Mediterranean. This leads us to the cut-off pool over the central Mediterranean. This is a good illustration of what should happen to the blocking pool over Canada. It should slide further and further south until it becomes cut off and the jet will reform to the north of it. These pools of cold air cut off aloft in lower latitudes are the reason for outbreaks of thunderstorms and the visitation of surface lows to areas that do not normally see very many.

To sum up:

(a)   the upper westerlies blow W to E

round the temperate latitudes of both hemispheres;

(b) long waves in them carousel round the poles in a general drift from west to east;

(c) if the wavelength gets longer than a critical distance (which at 45°N is something over 4000 miles), then a quasi-stationary blocking high will occupy one crest and/or a 'blocking' low will occupy an adjacent trough;

(d) as the wavelength lengthens, the systems drift retrograde, i.e. east to west;

(e) L on upper contours means low height, i.e. a depression in the undulations of the pressure surface. Conversely H indicates a warm dome where the contour heights are high.

(f) the fate of upper lows is to be cut off and abandoned over sub-tropical latitudes. The same fate attends highs over high latitudes.

4 UPPER WINDS AND TEMPERATURE

It might seem strange at first sight to approach surface weather from winds at levels way above our heads. Yet that is what we must do because the upper winds control the surface pressure pattern. It is upper winds that steer the surface depression centres and the travelling anticyclones. The way the long waves develop at 20 000–30 000 ft aloft determines whether the surface pressure pattern will be mobile or static. Where we see racetracks of contour lines on the upper charts is where the surface lows are most likely to develop and move. The positions of surface fronts follow a pattern that is linked to the jet stream which blows around 30 000 ft up. Thus the upper winds are crucial in our understanding of the surface weather and how it will develop and change.

The way the height of the 500 mb surface varied between the Great Lakes and the Caspian Sea along 45°N in fig. 3.2 is shown in fig. 4.1. The average temperature of the air column under the trough over Nova Scotia is seen to be low as cold air packs down into a shallower layer than warm air. Thus over Britain the average column temperature was high.

Comparing the contours in fig. 3.2 with the profile in fig. 4.1 we see a simple and helpful resemblance. We see that we can, within reason, look at the contours and imagine them projected on to the vertical along some line of latitude within their compass. The horizontal contour shapes resemble the profile they represent.

So we find the single most important connection between the way upper winds blow and the temperature of the air in their vicinity. For example, stand with your back to the wind blowing along the upper contours in mid-Atlantic and we see at once that upper winds blow to keep *low temperature* on their *left*. This simple idea will enable us to connect the winds at altitude with those at the surface which blow to keep low pressure on their left. The link between them comes from the temperature of the air masses that lie in their vicinity.

AIRMASSES

These are blocks of air of immense volume that originate in certain areas called source

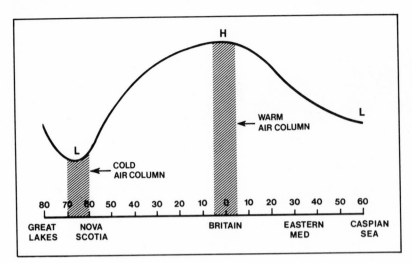

Fig. 4.1   *The way the height of the 500 mb surface changed across the Atlantic block shown in fig. 3.2. The vertical scale is very much enlarged.*

regions. To illustrate this we will take the two major airmasses of the North Atlantic Region. The cold wet one is the maritime Polar (mP) airmass which is air that has stagnated over the polar wastes and has acquired lower than average temperatures throughout its whole depth. It has also become relatively humid for its temperature. Thus it contains the necessary water vapour to fuel weather processes of the most virulent kind.

The other is the warm wet airmass that has stagnated over sub-tropical seas and in particular the region of the Sargasso Sea. It is called the maritime Tropical (mT) airmass and it has also acquired the attributes of its underlying source region, so becoming humid throughout its depth. Because warm air can hold more vapour than cold, so the potential amount of water vapour in mP air is very large, and its nasty habit of forming sea fog is well known.

All regions of the temperate latitudes will have their equivalents of these two airmasses, and it is predominantly from the clash of these two that the depressions are born. We will for now ignore the other airmasses that exist, but facts about them can be found under Airmasses in Part Two.

DEPRESSION FORMATION

The detailed theory of how depressions form is covered in Part Two. Here we can sketch the main sequence of events. The mP and the mT airmasses meet along the polar front. The textbook depression forms over the apex of a wave in the polar front, and fig. 4.2a is a representation of a classic low with the warm and cold fronts shown in vertical cross-section along the line ABCD. The path of the jet stream shows it snaking through the warm airmass at an altitude of some 30 000 ft (10 km) with the low centre many tens of miles to the south (NH) or north (SH). It goes through the fronts just within the warm air where there is a break in the tropopause. It is here, in the highest extremities of the warm and cold frontal wedges of warm air, that the cirrus clouds form, and they form on the equatorial side of the jet. The classic sequence of cloud types follow one another in as the warm front advances. These are

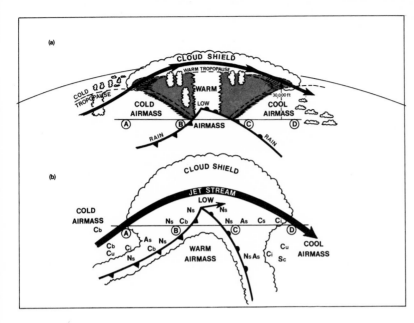

Fig. 4.2   (a) A vertical representation of the frontal cloud wedges and their relation to the jet stream. The frontal cross-sections stand vertically above the line ABCD while the jet snakes through and round them. (b) The plan view of the same situation showing where the line ABCD has been taken. The low is moving slightly north of east and will eventually arrive under the jet.

Ci   cirrus – hooks, banners, mare's tails (photos 5.1, C.1 and C.10)

Cs   cirrostratus – ring haloes about sun and moon (photo C.11)

As   altostratus – darker cloud into which the sun is gradually lost (photo C.12)

Ns   nimbostratus – the dark rain-bearing cloud of bad weather (photo C.14)

The sequence is more or less reversed as the cold front passes, but active (ana) cold fronts have heavy squally showers along their leading edges due to:

Cb   cumulonimbus – the deep unstable heap clouds that produce showers

and the Cs phase is not often very apparent along the trailing edges of cold fronts (photos 12.1 and C.15).

A plan view (fig. 4.2b) indicates the relative positions of the fronts, jet and cloud shield as seen from space. The two diagrams should be read in conjunction in order to obtain a visual three-dimensional impression of the anatomy of a developed but still developing depression.

In the map for 0000 7 November 1985

(fig. 4.3) the 300 mb contours have been added to the surface low and high centres. Across the north Atlantic the fronts form a continuous band of division between the two airmasses and this is paralleled in this case by another continuous line which extends right through northern Russia and into Siberia. The feature that has led to this twin development of what is normally only a single line of division is the cut-off pool (C) in mid-Atlantic, which is the same one we saw stretching down the east coast of the United States in fig. 3.2 and whose progress may be followed in the intervening period through the examples in chapter 6.

We have two contour racetracks, one south of the pool and the other north of it, of which the latter is the stronger. However, in accordance with the ideas given on page 23, the lows are developing under both these high-speed upper wind corridors. We also have two distinct masses of cold air aloft, with again the one to the north being colder than the one to the south. Thus the southerly part of the front has warm air to the south and cool to the north, whereas the northern part has cold air to the north of cool air. In both cases we have a temperature contrast from north to south which means the winds blow to keep lower temperature on the left and higher on the right.

No surface of division between two fluids of different densities can remain static, either vertically or horizontally. In the vertical the warm airmass must slope up over the cold and the cold must wedge in under the warm. This creates frontal surfaces. In the horizontal the long undisturbed parts of the polar front must develop waves which, given the right conditions, will develop into the frontal systems of lows that form at the apex of the waves.

Let us pick up the two lows in the Atlantic. Low A and Low B are both under different racetracks of contours and both are open-wave depressions. Because they are both under strong westerlies they can be expected to travel on converging courses towards the British Isles, but in particular note the way that the upper contours curve round the warm sector of Low B so that the upper winds are almost parallel to the fronts both ahead of and behind the depression. This is a classic example of the upper winds bending to keep warm air on their right.

The same kind of thing has happened to Low A, but the surface low and fronts have been rather left behind the ridge in the upper contours. Looking at the other major low (Low C) over Scandinavia, we see the same thing happening there with the upper winds parallel to the warm front, but not to the cold front.

Now none of these lows is a really major

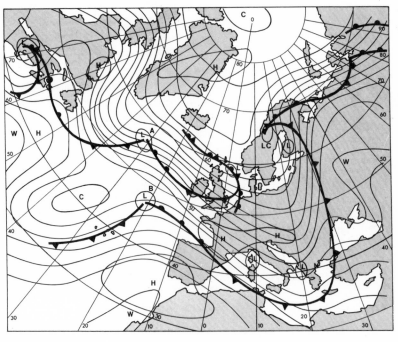

Fig. 4.3   *Two polar fronts? This is what happens sometimes, but the message of this diagram is that contours bend round warm sectors. C and W stand for cold pools and warm domes, respectively.*

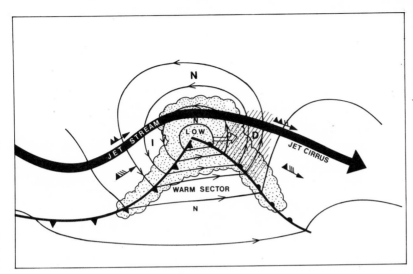

Fig. 4.4 *The relationship between the way jet cirrus moves compared with the wind near the surface yields a most important forecasting tool.*

feature, but when a depression forms that is going to deepen and induce gale or severe gales, the contrast in the airmass temperatures is near its maximum and the relation between the surface low and the upper winds becomes more like Fig. 4.4.

Features of this tie-up between surface and upper winds include:

(a) the developing low centre is found on the equatorial side of the jet stream;
(b) the jet and the surrounding wind field blow to enclose the warm sector, i.e. keep low temperature on the left and high on the right.

In this simple textbook case we will introduce ideas that will help us forecast our own weather for some hours ahead and with some chance of getting it right.

Ahead of a developing low centre the signs of deterioration in the situation will lie in the way the high-level winds advance from the left of the gradient wind. Wher-

ever more or less square boxes are formed through the crossing of isobars and the contours, so as to obey the above rule, the weather is set to deteriorate. They are marked D for deterioration.

When the centre of the depression has passed and the winds swing in from the NW, the same sort of square boxes form, but here the weather is going to improve. The orientation of upper to lower winds is now in the opposite sense. That means that wherever the high clouds behind the cold front can be seen moving from the right hand of the gradient wind, we can write I for improvement.

We also see that to the north and south of the centre the isobars are parallel to the contours or anti-parallel to them. These are largely neutral (N) areas where no change is to be expected for a few hours. That rule needs some qualification in practice, but it is valid for this introduction.

5 LOOKING FOR BAD WEATHER

It is of the utmost importance to the yachtsman at sea to recognise the signs of a developing depression well before the weather deteriorates to a point where he is forced to seek shelter or gain searoom to ride out the storm. Luckily nature provides easily recognised clues that trouble is brewing long before that trouble arrives.

The jet stream, which indicates the likelihood of a depression developing, is recognisable to the observer on the ground in several ways. First, it is accompanied by the form of ice clouds which are called jet-stream cirrus (photos C.1 and C.2).

Jet cirrus is formed in great profusion by the processes going on near the jet stream. For instance the jet is found below the tropopause, but in the warm airmass, and the process of Ci formation demands a relatively high moisture concentration even at a height of 6 miles. This the wet 'warm' airmass can provide, and it grows vast numbers of individual ice-crystal 'shower' clouds which have been set off by the ascending warm air. The showers of ice that fall out of the cirrus heads form the fallstreaks that give cirrus its unique shape.

In the middle right of photo 5.1 we see excellent examples of individual Ci clouds with the fallstreaks falling into slower wind below the heads and so becoming left behind. This gives Ci its characteristic hooked appearance. The shallower the hook the stronger the wind at head level, and so the more likely it is that the Ci is formed in association with a high-speed jet. As we descend, wind speed falls from its maximum in the jet (see fig. 8.2). This is called the 'wind shear', and we see that if the wind did not change with height there would be no shear, and fallstreaks would drop vertically down through the atmosphere. We may see them doing this before the outbreak of thunder as then the winds are light aloft. Light upper winds are a necessary requisite for thunderstorms because otherwise the storms get ripped apart and cannot organize their updraughts.

At the other end of the scale, hooked Ci, where the fallstreak appears to stream back straight out of the base of the cirrus head, indicates maximum wind shear. In the photo we see a distinct gap between the level of the streak and the head, so although

5.1   *Here we see cirrus over cumulus – a typical sky ahead of trouble. Note that a cirrus cloud is a head out of which a streak of ice crystals falls.*

there is wind shear it may not be of the strongest kind. However, do not neglect the message inherent in hooked Ci. Wind shear is a sure sign that a jet stream blows not far away on the polar side of the cirrus formations.

Note that in the photo we have no clouds between the Ci at some 30 000 ft altitude and the cumulus which is about 2000–3000 ft up. This is again characteristic of the sky ahead of developing bad weather. It is rare for any medium-level cloud to be present when the Ci is invading the sky. There is a vault which, once the cumulus has itself disappeared, is quite free of cloud other than that coming in at altitude.

At this time the surface wind may well be light, and if you are on land and it is evening or night it could well be calm. Overnight there is wind near the surface, but it is locked away above a surface inversion layer. Only when the gradient tightens to a sufficient degree can this wind appear at the surface.

At this time also the barometer may not have begun to fall, or if it is falling the fall is slow and erratic. With smaller, faster-moving lows than the one envisaged here, the barometer may be tumbling with the onset of the high cloud, and surface wind may well become moderate or even fresh. In this scenario the low whose cirrus we are observing is a full-blooded one not moving very fast because it is also deepening as it comes.

Some hundreds of miles ahead of the low centre, despite the ferocity of what is to come, it is often fair and pleasant – possibly just too little wind. The rate at which the cirrus invades the sky, however, gives clues as to the likely wind speeds later.

READING THE HIGH SKY

Whatever other cloud you may ignore in the sky, never ignore cirrus. It is the cloud that tells you most about what is going to happen, and it also gives you the maximum warning. The fallstreaks left behind by the onward-racing cirrus heads will show the wind at their level from the direction they point, and it is worth noting that they point towards the warm air both ahead of the warm front and behind the cold front of the depression.

When, as happens with jet cirrus, the ice showers in their sheer profusion amalgamate into immense banners of cloud that stretch across the sky – sometimes from horizon to horizon – the lie of these banners gives the direction of the wind at their altitude. This is most likely to be from NW to SE when an intense depression is routed your way (SW–NE in SH), and such banners only form in association with the jet. (Note that these banners can survive the jet with which they formed and so may appear in the sky from odd directions and without other signs of bad weather coming.) (Photo C.16.)

The banner form of dense jet cirrus is characteristic, but we need more clues before we commit ourselves to a forecast of a deterioration sufficiently bad to warrant seeking shelter.

The strongest jets form with the most actively developing depressions, and so the speed with which the cirrus moves across the sky is an important clue as to the severity or not of coming weather. It may be difficult if not impossible to judge the motion of cirrus elements from the deck of a yacht as you have no fixed reference points. You may be able to judge motion by reference to the sun or the moon, but nothing else is fixed. So generally we can say that if you can detect the Ci elements scudding across the high sky without any reference point, then the speed is 100 kn. or more. It is about 80 kn. when motion is just discernible. Sometimes, mainly in winter, you can see the cirrus near a jet literally shooting across the sky, and you then know that the jet is near its maximum speed of about 180 kn.

The rule says 'The stronger the jet the "stronger" the weather to come'. This is because the jet speeds increase as the difference in temperature between the cold and warm airmasses increases. Such contrast tends to invigorate the surface weather:

makes fronts sharp and active, makes the prospect of sea fog in the warm air the more likely, etc. In particular the wind regime of the lows that form near the jet is normally going to be at its most active.

It must be emphasised before we proceed any further that we may be talking about those, luckily rare, rogue lows that cause the loss or wreck of even well-found yachts. We will be able to use very similar principles on the much more numerous depressions that need not lead to survival conditions. However, what are and what are not survival conditions depend on the state of the crew in most instances. What to the well-honed racing crew is an inconvenience may well be near disaster conditions for the family cruiser. So it is to help all and sundry recognise the big ones that I am addressing these remarks.

DEVELOPMENT OF THE SITUATION

Because the barometer may not be a very good guide to the severity of coming weather, and cirrus clouds come with all sorts of different weather conditions, it is important to recognise also those situations where the weather is set to deteriorate in a large-scale way.

Such deterioration not only includes the onset of warm fronts or occlusions, but also the deepening of an existing low or the formation of a new one. These events constitute development, and development also embraces the building of highs and ridges when the cyclonic weather has passed.

We expect lows to form and deepen a few hundred miles on the equatorial side of the jet axis, and we have cirrus clouds to indicate the direction and speed of the winds at jet levels. We may, if we have a facsimile printer, have 300 mb and surface weather charts on the same scale and covering the same area. Such charts form

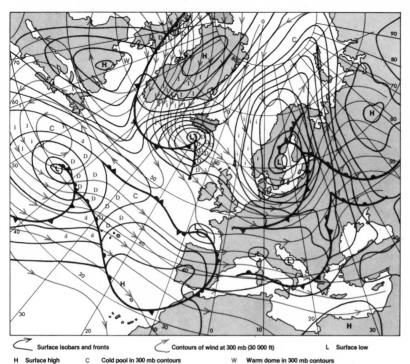

Fig. 5.1 *How the high-level winds and the gradient winds provide reliable forecasts of where the weather will deteriorate (D) or improve (I). This is for 0000Z 3 November 1985.*

Surface isobars and fronts	Contours of wind at 300 mb (30 000 ft)	L Surface low
H Surface high C Cold pool in 300 mb contours	W Warm dome in 300 mb contours	
D Areas of strong cyclonic development	I Areas of anticyclonic development	d and i Areas of lower development

part of the daily output of fax stations across the world. We are going to use a sequence of such charts received between 3 and 6 November 1985 from the European fax station, Offenbach. These will illustrate the ideas of development and indicate how the observer even without upper-air charts can, for his own area, recognise the developing situation from sky observation.

The charts as I received them on a Nagrafax with a kilometric receiver using a ferrite aerial are just the right size to be slipped into the 30 cm × 22 cm pockets of a transparent wallet file, and such a file or something similar is essential if the easily crushable charts are to be preserved. Such a system is also essential if the areas of development are to be identified easily. We also need to discover where the immobile parts of the chart are – the quasi-stationary lows and highs.

The 300 mb chart gives the winds at

something over 30 000 ft, and so the cirrus clouds we observe from the ground will be riding these winds. At this height we are above the level to which the travelling surface lows and highs can reach and so modify the upper winds. Thus, where we find closed contours in association with closed isobars round surface lows and highs, we can be sure that a great tube of rotating winds exists from the surface to over 30 000 ft. Such tubes can only exist if the vertical axis of the whole system is not moving very much.

Quasi-stationary areas of high and low pressure are the fulcrums of the chart, and in fig. 5.1 we can identify one of each over or near America. Because the upper contour chart is so much simpler than the surface chart, I traced the 300 mb contours for 0000 3 November on the wallet file's transparent surface using a water-based pen designed for use with the acetate sheets of overhead projectors (red contour lines with arrows in fig. 5.1). I then slipped the corresponding surface chart under this, lined the two up and noted that the high over Nova Scotia was largely immobile and the low near 40N 40W was also unable to move.

Deep troughs in the contours such as exist from Scandinavia down into central Europe are also areas where surface lows cannot move much, so the low over the Gulf of Bothnia is not going very far in the next 24 hours. It is lows and highs under long runs of contours (i.e. strong upper winds above them or near them) that are the likely candidates for development. However, if the low over Scandinavia cannot move, then the one south of Iceland cannot move much either. Yet if it is thwarted in movement it will certainly deepen.

We can get an idea of how much in the following way. We see in the idealised situation in fig. 4.4 that ahead of the developing low centre the surface isobars and the upper contours form more or less square boxes. We have to seek such areas on our charts to find the zones of maximum cyclonic development. Here the weather will in general worsen. This is where the barometer will be falling most steeply, and it is the area into which the low centre will move.

Conversely, behind the cold front of the travelling low, the isobars and contours make square boxes, but the winds they define are orientated to one another in the opposite sense to where the cyclonic development was taking place. Thus behind the retreating low there is anticyclonic development and the weather is set to improve. This improvement will include the clearance of the cold front and the eventual damping out of the showers that are so often found in this region of the chart. It may well lead to the establishment of a ridge of high pressure or even a full anticyclone with the consequent lessening of wind strengths and the arrival of settled weather.

Because it is the character of the weather that is of importance to us, we will mark the cyclonic boxes D for deterioration (you may prefer D to mean cyclonic development). In any case these are the zones where the weather-making processes will be moving towards more wind, more cloud and the outbreak of precipitation, be it rain or snow, etc.

We will mark the anticyclonic boxes I for improvement (or you may prefer I to indicate high or ridge intensifying), and note that the more square the two sets of lines are to one another the more intense the improvement will be. Also we will mark peripheral areas where the boxes are still cyclonic or anticyclonic but at a more acute angle d and i respectively to indicate lesser development. The regions where the surface isobars and upper contours are more or less parallel will be marked N for neutral.

THE MESSAGE IN THE WINDS

By using the flight path of cirrus to indicate direction and speed of the 300 millibar winds compared with the motion of cumulus, stratocumulus or any other low cloud, the observer can write these same letters for deterioration or improvement in his own patch of sky: he does not need charts to indicate whether he is in a zone of cyclonic or anticyclonic development. See photo C.6.

It is evident from fig. 4.4 that the following rule applies where the upper and lower winds cross for cyclonic development:

(a)   Stand back to the gradient wind and the upper wind comes from your left hand.

This is the orientation for deteriorating weather situations and it applies to lesser systems than the one we are considering.

Where the winds cross for anticyclonic development:

(b)   Stand back to the gradient wind and

the upper wind comes from your right hand.

This reverse orientation is for improving weather and it is also found where an anticyclone is building across a region.

To help the lone observer read the message in the winds correctly we can give a mnemonic thus:

Low weather from the *left* hand

Right weather from the *right* hand

As these rules apply to the Northern Hemisphere, all we have to do is to face the wind in the Southern Hemisphere and the rules again work.

I know from many years' experience how valuable these 'crossed-winds' rules are, as I have relied on them myself and have used them on innumerable occasions to elucidate' the way the weather will develop. I have tested them on Australian weather systems and have found that, as modified by facing the wind, they work equally well in the Southern Hemisphere as they do in the Northern.

I have used a bad weather system of the worst kind to introduce the crossed-winds rules, but it is important to realise that they work on many lesser troughs and ridges and they are of great use in thundery situations where it is not very obvious whether or not there will be actual thunder or perhaps just showers or even merely a cloud build-up which passes without incident.

Let me describe one such which occurred fairly recently. It was Friday morning 29 November 1985 and the morning forecast was full of the fact that it had been the coldest November night in central England for over forty years. Now there was, from the previous night's TV forecast, a small low poised to move from near Ireland down through the English Channel and to bring us, probably, some snow as it moved through to the south of my home in northeast Essex.

Observing the sky after breakfast I noted that the cirrus we had was moving from W just fast enough for it to be noticeable without resort to a 'nephoscope', i.e. something fixed by which to judge the cloud movement. So it was a slow jet speed of about 80 kn. There were several useful vapour trails formed by airliners flying high in the air corridor which helped to confirm the wind speed and direction. In the north-western sky there was what looked like old jet cirrus as it fanned out of the horizon.

Catching a glimpse of smoke drifting from a chimney I was able to see that the wind, though very light, was from NE. Allowing for the effect of the surface obstacles (page 49), that made the gradient wind easterly – in direct opposition to the upper westerly. This indicated at once that the low would track through to the south and also that the chances of any snow in our area were minimal. We can see why I came to this conclusion from looking at the winds to the north of the depression in fig. 4.4.

In the event my forecast proved right, for although it clouded up during the day no precipitation of any kind fell. There was, as we see, no sign of development in the orientation of the upper and lower winds and so the chances of snow or rain were very low.

The use of the crossed-winds rules on these lesser systems will be extended in a later chapter, but for now we will follow the way the situation of fig. 5.1 developed and consider what it can show us that will strengthen our confidence in the universality of the rules. It is important to realise that it matters not if you are in the county of Norfolk in England, in Norfolk in the American state of Virginia, or in Novgorod in Russia: the same rules apply. The swathe of temperate latitudes where the vast majority do their sailing is where the crossed-winds rules work best. Go further south into the tropics and you cannot expect to be able to use them in quite the same way. They are formulated for the roundabout of pressure systems that swirl across the globe between about 30°N or S and 60°N or S.

Before we leave this introduction to the way the orientation of upper and lower winds helps us sort out the development of the weather, we must not forget the neutral zones where the lower and upper winds are more or less parallel. Such regions have been marked N in fig. 4.4 and we see that both to the north and to the south of the low centre we get neutral orientation. It is here that nothing is happening either way to the weather, and it indicates that for a while nothing will happen. However, note that where the upper and lower winds are travelling in the same direction, the low centre is to the north, and where they are in opposition it is to the south. Readers in the SH will have to reverse north for south and vice versa.

The next chapter illustrates in detail how the forecast method based on the crossing of upper and lower winds can be used to make sense out of a developing situation. At a first reading the reader might be advised to skip chapter 6 and go on to chapter 7. There are, however, some very important ideas contained in chapter 6 which those who wish to use the crossed-winds method to forecast their own weather should not miss, and wrestling with this chapter will be very beneficial to them.

6   CASE OF A BREAKAWAY LOW

At the beginning of November 1985 the long warm autumn that followed a long wet summer was still hanging on in England and Northern France. The chart (fig. 5.1) was dominated by quasi-stationary systems with a low south of Iceland very slow-moving and another in the western Atlantic largely pinned to its 40N 40W position by being more or less under an upper low there.

However, when we look for the areas of cyclonic development (D) we find them stretching eastwards into the Atlantic with little anticyclonic development (I) to speak of behind. Thus we must expect the low to elongate west–east while the fronts come on driven by the upper winds to the south of the low. If the succeeding charts showed a continuation of the cyclonic development tendency, then there was every prospect that a new centre of low pressure would develop on the point of occlusion.

Twelve hours later what we expected from gridding the previous chart had come to pass, but the cyclonic development ahead of the fronts had increased in extent and this system was showing signs of joining with

the slow-moving low to the north. The risk of a breakaway low was still very much there (fig. 6.1).

We can test the efficiency of our method by first identifying the D and I areas on the midnight charts. We can then plot the fall or rise of pressure around the chart in the following 12 hours to see if the latter were forecast by the crossed-winds rules. We find that the D/I boxes in most cases accurately identified the regions where pressure would fall or rise so that anyone in those areas who was reading the high sky and crossing the upper wind with the gradient wind would have been warned of deterioration or promised improving conditions.

The reader will see that in fig. 6.1 the black hatched areas around the low south of Iceland do not cover the areas where pressure fell most in the 12 hours. However, the method of gridding the 300 mb with the surface chart only gives the situation at the time when it is done – in this case the early hours of 3 November – and does not allow for changes either in the surface or in the upper air during the forecast period. Thus when a D area is

Fig. 6.1 *How things developed in the 12 hours between 0000 and 1200Z 3 November 1985. The black hatched areas and the centres and fronts are taken from fig. 5.1 and show where things should have been on the move. We can see if the expected happened • from the coloured fronts and centres and the circled figures which give the falls (black) and rises (coloured) that actually occurred during the 12 hours. The low in mid-Atlantic is the important one: it did as expected.*

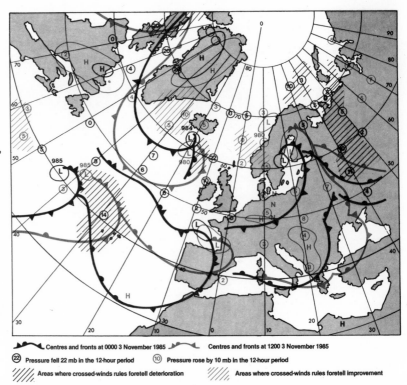

⌒⌒ Centres and fronts at 0000 3 November 1985	⌒⌒ Centres and fronts at 1200 3 November 1985
㉒ Pressure fell 22 mb in the 12-hour period	⑩ Pressure rose by 10 mb in the 12-hour period
///// Areas where crossed-winds rules foretell deterioration	///// Areas where crossed-winds rules foretell improvement

recognised from the crossing of the winds and the situation is mobile, we have to allow for the advance of that area forwards into areas where there is, as yet, no apparent deterioration. Here your barometer may warn you possibly before the high clouds do.

The D areas over Russia coupled to the I area around Norway (although the latter is small) indicate the development of a cyclonic situation over Russia without it being necessarily due to the movement of the lows over the Gulf of Bothnia. It is likely that the frontal system (now divorced from its parent low) that is nearest to, and threading through the lower part of, that cyclonic development area will bring in the airmass that can induce the formation of a new low-pressure system over there.

Do not expect this simple method to be perfect. For instance, down through Scandinavia and down into Poland the upper and lower winds were in the same direction giving a neutral (N) zone and yet the pressure rose in that area. However, that is an error in the right direction as it moved towards improvement rather than deterioration. It is my experience that when the cirrus and the gradient wind blow in the same direction, the weather does often get better and not worse. Thus as, from a practical point of view, the most important situation is one that is moving towards worsening weather, and we find that those cyclonic developments are well forecast by our method, we must be thankful for that and not expect miracles from what is, after all, a relatively simple way of doing some pretty accurate forecasting.

With charts from the fax, the way the surface chart would develop should have become evident. For instance the high over Greenland should slip southwards into the I area and, as the rises in pressure north of

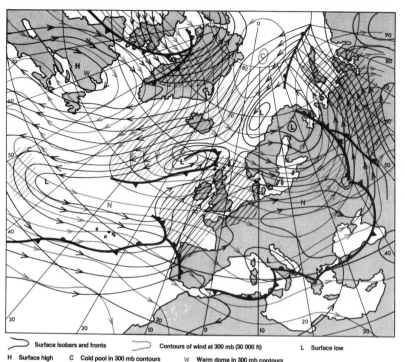

Fig. 6.2   *The gradient and upper winds compared at 0000Z 4 November. The high over Newfoundland cannot move; the low south of Iceland will not move either. The low at 40N 40W has, as expected, stayed roughly where it was but its fronts have zoomed on towards Iberia. With crossed-winds deterioration showing up all over Biscay, Britain and the North Sea, we can expect some bad weather to develop.*

Surface isobars and fronts	Contours of wind at 300 mb (30 000 ft) L Surface low
H Surface high C Cold pool in 300 mb contours	W Warm dome in 300 mb contours
//// Area of cyclonic development ///// Areas of anticyclonic development	XXXX Areas of lesser development

Scotland show, the low south of Iceland cannot move very far eastwards. So the winds on its northern side must increase to severe gale or even storm force. We also see from fig. 6.1 that the low sat and deepened slowly over the 12 hours while pressure fell in the D zone ahead of it and also to the south of it. Interestingly enough none of these falls greatly changed the winds. It must be realised that even 22 mb in 12 hours as occurred north-west of Scotland is less than 2 mb per hour and so should only amount to about Force 6. However, in association with the falls ahead of the mid-Atlantic quasi-stationary low, this bridge of falling pressure between the two systems indicated that something was brewing here for later.

Almost of as much interest as crossed winds are the parallel winds which promise neutrality. There was a noticeable parallelism between the upper and lower winds in

the region of Newfoundland, and for the next 12 hours no change of pressure occurred in that region whereas in the I region to the south pressure rose steadily. In the region of 40N 50W the winds had to increase, as with pressure rising one side and not falling the other the gradient had to tighten.

With the mid-Atlantic low held back (but pressure falling to the east of it) 'troughing' as it is called had to be taking place towards Spain. Such elongated troughs with fronts in them are candidates ripe for the development of a new low on the point of occlusion. Would it happen?

The fourth of November

Our technique for forecasting the way the chart will develop worked pretty well over the 12 hours covering the times of figs 5.1 and 6.1. The high over Newfoundland stayed fixed. The cold pool (C) over the

Atlantic low did not allow it to move so it was still stuck over 40N 40W at midnight of 3 November (0000 of 4 November: fig. 6.2). However, its fronts, being under a contour racetrack, swept on so that the warm front was now over Portugal.

By again gridding with the 300 mb contour chart we find that a large D zone now joins the areas northeastwards of these fronts to the similar areas ahead of the low south of Iceland. To confirm this we find that in the next 12 hours the pressure fell over the areas of Biscay, the British Isles and the North Sea. However, the falls were not dramatic, amounting to less than a millibar per hour on average at the most (fig. 6.3).

The most important feature, and the one we set out to find, was the development, off Brest, of a definite low centre on the point of occlusion of the fronts we had been following across the Atlantic. The low

south of Iceland also began to move and was north of Scotland by midday of 4 November. It seemed most likely from the large D area between them that these two centres would somehow merge into a generally cyclonic area covering Britain.

Meanwhile in the improvement zone that was indicated south-west of Iceland pressure rose, but the effect of the low over Baffin Bay was already making itself felt with pressure falling west of Iceland. The effect here was (by midnight) to turn the high of the previous day into a ridge from the quasi-stationary high over Newfoundland and to replace it with a trough from the low over Baffin Bay by midday. Once again in fig. 6.3 we see how our D and I zones fairly accurately foretold the major changes in pressure on the chart and so indicated the areas where weather would deteriorate or improve.

Fig. 6.3 *The way the situation developed in the 12 hours 0000–1200Z 4 November. By midday on the fourth a low centre had developed in Biscay.*

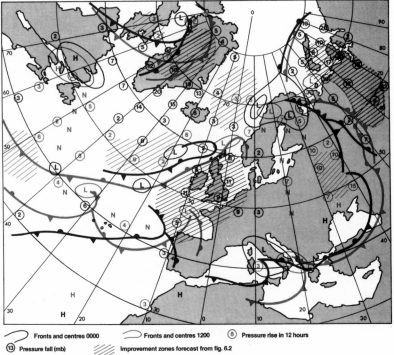

Fronts and centres 0000	Fronts and centres 1200	⑧ Pressure rise in 12 hours
⑬ Pressure fall (mb)	//// Improvement zones forecast from fig. 6.2	
//// Deterioration zones forecast from fig. 6.2	N Neutral zone (usually leads to improvement)	

The fifth of November

The midnight chart (fig. 6.4) showed the complexity of the cyclonic area covering Britain and France and extending into Norway. A very large area of deteriorating conditions spread right across Europe and Scandinavia while a lesser improvement zone built down from Iceland into Ireland and the seas to the west. The seas west of Spain took on a generally neutral look, and pressure did not vary much there in the next 12 hours. However, it was the pressure rises to the west and falls to the east of Britain that spelt strengthening winds with a generally northerly slant to them.

The low over Greenland reformed off Iceland in response to the insistent drive of the pressure falls off Iceland and the corresponding rises indicated by the I zone over Baffin Island. Here we see where our method may not always give the full answer because there were some reasonable falls of pressure south of Greenland of which the crossed winds there only gave a vague indication. However, from the mariner's point of view they were not enough to strengthen the winds to such an extent as to be a hazard. Thus such indeterminate regions need only lead to some fall of pressure and a minor wind increase. We cannot expect to rival the professional meteorologist's 15-layer model with our two-layer version. What is remarkable about our crossed-winds rules is that they work as well as they do, and combined with other clues they will give the lone sailing boat stuck vulnerably on the ocean a good idea of when things are going to get really sticky.

FORECASTING ON

We can use fig. 6.5 as an exercise in forecasting. As I live close by I will select the narrows of the southern North Sea as my forecast area.

We see pressure has fallen most (20 mb) in the D area over central England and Scandinavia (16 mb). In this figure we see

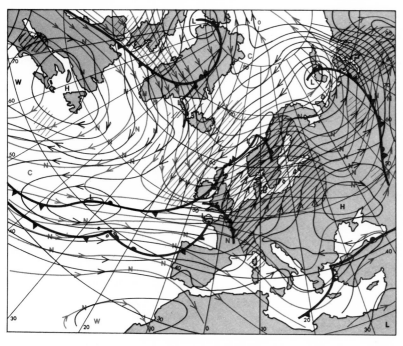

Fig. 6.4 *With low-pressure systems converging on Britain from west and south, strong winds had to develop in the Channel and the North Sea. This is the surface and 300 mb situation at 0000Z 5 November. Key as in fig. 6.3.*

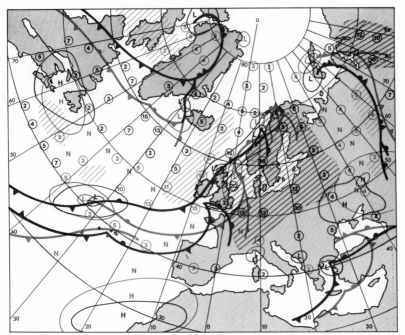

Fig. 6.5 *How the situation developed in the 12 hours 0000–1200Z 5 November. The sea areas around Britain are in for some strong wind with a cold northerly slant to it. The high over Newfoundland is making some progress south eastwards into the Atlantic. Key as in fig. 6.3.*

that the whole of Biscay area is static. Thus the gradient must increase northwards across the North Sea. However, the strongest increase in the gradient is between southern Ireland (where there is a rise of 15 mb) and Denmark.

Thus we expect winds at first to strengthen from the west as the complex set of fronts and lows around Britain rationalise themselves into one system, to be followed by even stronger wind from NW when the cold front, looped down through northern France at midday, has fully cleared through.

At 6 a.m. there were broken skies over the southern North Sea, and the feel of the morning indicated that, together with the rain that had fallen earlier, a warm front had passed. The wind blew hard across the region during the day – enough to demolish the roof of a new hypermarket being built in my local town of Colchester – and on into the evening to the accompaniment of the whizzes and bangs of the bonfire parties of Guy Fawkes Night.

Thus eventually the expectations of the

day before yesterday came to fruition. The breakaway low had not amounted to much on its own, but when added to the cyclonic area of the low to its north it had contributed to the first strong wind over my own area in several weeks. Using such a possibly minor entity to illustrate the crossed-winds method is in some ways more useful than selecting some deep and vigorous depression as an example. Most people will know and be told in advance of such systems. It is the smaller – less publicised – weather systems that the sailor has to contend with for most of the time. Here we see how one such was forecast, and also we have indicated what interpretations to place on the clues that the method provides.

To gain maximum advantage from this sequence of charts the reader will have to work through them slowly, asking whether the crossed-winds clues would have foretold the events as they happened. The crossed-winds-rule method of personal forecasting involves having two things that may not necessarily be there. These are high clouds and holes in the lower clouds through which to see them.

With a fax machine this problem is solved by doing (for limited areas of interest) just what has been done here. For the lone observer it may represent a stumbling block. However, although it is good to know about the movement and development of minor systems, it has been pointed out that when the big low hoves in sight its dynamics lead to clearing skies ahead of it and so the high cirrus can be seen. This may

occur with lesser systems, but we hope they will not be as important to life and limb even if banks of low cloud do obscure the incoming higher cloud. Thus in practice the crossed-winds approximation to gridding the surface and 300 mb charts stands us in good stead because it works best when it is needed most. Anyone who thinks he has a crossed-winds orientation for cyclonic development over his area will obviously seek a forecast from the available sources. Forewarned he will be forearmed.

7 CHARTING THE NEXT TWELVE HOURS

It has been shown in the sequence of charts in chapter 6 how the crossed-winds rules will help forecast the likely changes in the weather scene wherever you are. It was made clear there that although you can do some important personal forecasting wherever you can see cirrus clouds crossing your sky, there are going to be many occasions when lower cloud obscures the high sky. Such occasions usually go with weather that is not going to produce gales, but it is important to be able to assess the state of the larger weather scene from whatever charts you may be able to see. We can best illustrate the techniques through taking another example from the same period as the sequence of chapter 6, but back in October when the upper wind pattern was still showing its blocking characteristics and the blocking high had not yet quite forsaken Atlantic Europe.

The surface features (in black) and the upper contours (in red) for 0000Z Friday 25 October 1985 are shown in fig. 7.1. Let us pick out the important features, remembering that the contours give the winds around 30 000 ft and the isobars the wind at

about 2000 ft.

First, identify the centres that are immobile. These are found wherever the closed contours and closed isobars roughly coincide in position. We find two major ones:

(a) the quasi-stationary low (L_D) out on the Atlantic south of Greenland;
(b) the quasi-stationary high (H_D) centred over the German/Polish border.

Whatever other features there are surrounding these centres will tend to move round them under the impetus of the upper winds. The deep trough in the upper westerlies stretching down from Greenland is one good reason why there can be a blocking high over Europe: there is no direct feed of lows from America out into the Atlantic as the trough is preventing it. Another is the long wave in the westerlies (chapter 3) which is of such a wavelength as to allow the upper wind pattern to go to sleep and not move on round the hemisphere as is more usual.

Without upper charts, the way to come to the same conclusion is to follow a sequence of charts through a newspaper or from the TV and it will soon become evident where the motion is and where things are quasi-stationary.

Secondly, locate the centres that are under racetracks of contours. These are the mobile lows and highs, and in the case of lows we can find where the most closely spaced isobars are and so locate the jet-stream axis. This has been thickened in the figure. We remember that low centres on the equatorial side of jets deepen and develop; those whose fronts have their apex under the jet are about to occlude and so should not deepen further, and those with centres to the polar side of the jet are already occluding and filling.

Thus Low C between Norway and Greenland is about to occlude, and although

Fig. 7.1   *The situation at 0000Z 25 October 1985, to illustrate the foregoing ideas in use on a different situation. This is a blocking pattern.*

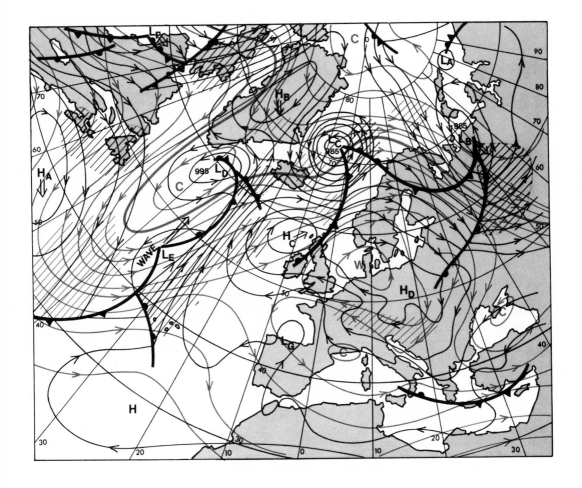

a major feature it should not become more nasty than it is already. However, it must travel with the racetrack, unlike Low D, the quasi-stationary low off Greenland whose centre will remain where it is while its fronts under the racetrack will swing on out of its circulation to eventually become one of those disembodied frontal systems we find on charts that cannot be seen to belong to any particular low centre.

This immobile low centre is what we will call a 'melting-pot' in that it will often absorb any other mobile lows that swim into its maw. That is what is about to be the fate of the wave low (Low E) in mid-Atlantic. However, other considerations indicate that it will form a new elongated low centre with Low D.

Again, without charts like this, you have to monitor a sequence of media charts to see what is moving and what is not. The problem with strings of lows, however, is that they change so rapidly that all you can identify in most cases is a corridor through which the succession of lows is passing and not expect to keep track of each low and its fronts from day to day. If you can, all well and good, but the modern-day chart-drawers are not hidebound by textbook situations as they used to be, and now, with satellite pictures to help them, can locate the frontal systems over the oceans in an *ad hoc* way. If it is seen to be there, they put it in, and so to the casual observer magical and mystifying transformations occur from one chart to the next. Over the 24 hours between newspaper charts and between TV weathercasts, much can happen so that even what are apparently easily recognisable and almost textbook situations become trans-formed and can hardly be recognised. This is something that the layman has to live with. It is another reason why all the coded charts that are fluxing through the airwaves at any moment need to be at the call of the yachtsman at sea so that this constant plethora of revision is known to him as soon as is practicable. We are not seeing

that yet, but it must come unless the late twentieth century sailor is to be left hope-lessly behind all other interested mariners.

In the meantime the way to divine development of the weather situation is to use the crossed-winds rules, and we find the areas where these rules would have foretold what would happen from fig. 7.1.

Starting right and ignoring Low A, Low B shows cyclonic development to south-east of it and anticyclonic to north-west of it and so should slide southeast-wards with the fronts moving on fast into central Asia.

Low C has strong cyclonic development ahead to the north-east and equally strong anticyclonic to the south-west, and so will track on to the north of Scandinavia. The fronts of Low D will get stretched out northwestward as the centre is not allowed to move. If Low C is moving away and Low D is stuck, the central area between them must see rising pressure which is what the crossed winds north of Iceland say. Thus High B will extend its influence southwards.

Almost nothing can happen to High D over central Europe, but High C centred over Scotland should drift northeastwards somewhat. This is shown by the cyclonic development orientation of the winds to the west of Ireland, and that in its turn will slacken the very strong southerly winds up the central Atlantic.

High A off the eastern seaboard of the USA will build eastwards into the Atlantic, while Low F just appearing over northern Canada must extend its influence out over Baffin Island and Baffin Bay as there is cyclonic development there. The low itself may not move far, but its fronts, being under a racetrack of contours, will move on steadily, probably leaving the parent low behind.

What actually happened is shown in fig. 7.2 where the surface chart for 12 hours later than fig. 7.1 has been superimposed on the fronts and centres as they were at mid-

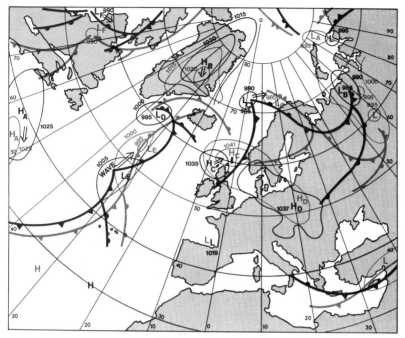

Fig. 7.2 *How the situation developed in the next 12 hours. The major low south of Greenland could not move and neither could the high over Europe. When that happens nothing much else can move either. Yet the crossed-winds method indicated small changes where they occurred.*

night previously. They show that we could have foretold the chart pretty accurately using our ideas of how to recognise fixed and mobile centres and how to see the areas of cyclonic and anticyclonic development.

We have only chanced our arm out to 12 hours ahead, and we do not have the two charts for some hours after the 'verification time' of 0000. The mariner hungry for information can in Europe obtain charts with the observations plotted, but not analysed, within two hours of the verification times of 0000, 0300, 0600, 0900, 1200, 1500, 1800 and 2100Z. If he wanted to do what we have just been doing above, he will have to wait until half the forecast period has gone before he has North Atlantic charts on the same scale for surface and 300 mb. He will only get them twice a day based on the VTs of 0000 and 1200. In America the Norfolk VA transmitter produces similar charts at about the same GMT times as Offenbach on which the analysis of development could be done. These charts will of course come out at ESTs, which are

five hours earlier than the GMT times, i.e. both charts will be out by 8 a.m. and 8 p.m.

I do not envisage the average yachtsman who may have a fax receiver doing, on the grand scale, what is being done here. The analysis has been done to show that the simple crossed-winds method works on most occasions, and to indicate how to interpret the observations you make.

Now, having explained how the large-scale features of the chart can be understood, we must move on into more detailed realms and this will be done as far as possible through as brief a description of the weather features as possible, amplified with ready-reference tables which will suggest to the mariner the questions he should be asking. It may be that no answers are forthcoming, but half the battle with a complex subject like met. is won when you at least know what the questions are.

We will start with descriptions of fronts and how to recognise what wind shifts, etc. will normally be experienced when they approach and pass.

8 USING CIRRUS TO READ THE UPPER WINDS

It has been shown in the examples of chapters 6 and 7 that we can make accurate assessments of the likely development of the weather situation from the way the cirrus-level winds blow compared with the winds near the surface. Now we want to know how to make these observations as accurately as possible bearing in mind that the sky may be viewed either from ashore or afloat.

It is going to be impossible to describe all the variations in cirrus skies, so only those that are truly prognostic for bad or better will be covered. Experience will show the observer which skies are and which are not good forecasting tools.

JET CIRRUS SKY

The longest, hottest summer on record in England came to an end about 13 September 1976. The jet streams had forsaken Europe for months and the cirrus of photo C.1 heralded their return. It blew Force 11 in the sea areas around the British Isles over the next couple of days, but the coming intense-depression weather was readable from the shape, speed and motion of the cirrus that streamed in from the north-west.

The recognition points are:

(a) the long parallel plumes or banners (the 'mare's tails' of the weather lore);
(b) the denseness of the banners (like the ones on the far horizon);
(c) their speed (which of course cannot be shown on a single picture);
(d) a clean line of division between cloud and no cloud. (The clear sky is on the poleward side in either hemisphere.) Photo C.1 does not show this feature but C.2 does.

We are going to imagine that the sky is being constantly monitored from when the first cirrus elements begin to appear to when the jet sky is fully formed. Then you are likely to be able to see the division between cloud and no cloud, which is often so sharp as to be as if cut with a knife, before the cirrus covers the whole sky. At other times jet cirrus becomes so dense that it almost looks like water-drop cloud, i.e.

the banners get thick enough to cut off direct light from the sky and so do gain some shadowing underneath – it is usually said that cirrus never shows any shadows. However, such dense jet cirrus is very rare, but it is my experience that when you see it you are in for a blow of the first magnitude.

When the jet speeds are of the order of 150 kn., the cirrus motion as a whole is in the same direction as the banners lie, but with lesser speeds the direction of movement of the mass can be at an angle to the apparent direction of the banners. You should take the mass motion as the correct one for using the crossed-winds rules. This fact is worth noting in the case of old jet cirrus that may look like photo C.2 in many ways, but which often moves in a wind field that is widely different in direction to the lie of the clouds.

Aircraft trails are formed at cirrus height and are of very great help in reading the upper winds. First, they provide a definite line of cloud that can be followed. The two photos C.3 and C.4 were taken at about the same time as photo C.1 but looking across the cirrus banners. They were taken within half a minute of one another, and you can see how far the trail has moved in that time by comparing its position with those of the trees below.

Trails that are across the wind will shred sideways and their very persistence will show that the air at their level is relatively wet. Persistent trails that form in clear upper sky should make you think that real cirrus cannot be long delayed. In this way they give you even longer warning of possible trouble than the cirrus itself.

Trails will also indicate wind direction by forming turret-tops along the back of the trail when the wind is roughly blowing parallel to the trail (photo C.5). If the wind is across the trail, as already said, it will spread out and widen. We can see how this has happened in a very short time to the trail in photos C.3 and C.4 because it is across a very strong upper wind.

You can get a rough idea of the wind speed by using an idea I call the 'thumb nephoscope'. You hold your thumb outstretched at arm's length against the sky and count the seconds for a cirrus element (or a trail) to travel the length of your thumb nail. I worked this out on a nail which is ¾ inch long at 2 ft from the eye, and for clouds around 30 000 ft the results are as follows:

Time to travel across thumb nail (s)	Speed (kn.)
3	180
4	140
5	110
6	90
7	80
8	70
9	60
10	55

You cannot expect exact results, but the thumb nephoscope does provide a useful guide though it is not much use for the slower speeds as your arm grows tired with being stuck up in the air and begins to wave about. Also you cannot use this at sea as you need to be on a stable surface. Still, you may well want to assess the prospects of a blow before you set sail rather than when you are at sea and so the idea is worth advancing.

When you look at a cirrus sky there will be parts of the cloud field that may not conform to the general run of the main body of cloud. You have to ignore these minor deviations and concentrate on the way the sky runs as a whole, and sometimes it is hard to tell whether a banner of cirrus is a true one formed by the ascending air along a frontal surface, or is simply an aircraft trail that has spread to look like one. However, in photos C.3 and C.4 there is no doubt that the clouds in the middle distance are indicating, by their fallstreaks, the true direction of the wind up there and that the bright banner stretched across them is an aircraft trail.

What the edge of the jet cirrus looks like

from space is shown in photo 8.1 which was taken by the polar orbiting satellite NOAA 6 in the visible at 0909 GMT 16 October 1981 (Ref. 4). The edge is quite sharp as the shadow on England shows, and fig. 8.1 shows the jet core and an associated depression with a high over northern Europe and a ridge over Britain. The thick lines are the contours of the 300 mb surface and so show the direction of the upper winds. We see the D orientation well established ahead of the low with gradient winds across the south-west approaches from SSE and the jet from WSW.

A cross-section along the line AB (fig. 8.1) covering some 1000 Nm shows the characteristic break in the tropopause with the jet just inside the warm airmass and the frontal zone with dryer stratospheric air within it stretching down towards the surface. Where the cirrus layer was is shown shaded. The reader might find it instructive to attempt to draw the jet to scale as it is 2.5 Nm deep and 150 Nm wide. The result is a flat tube of wind which is always going to be misrepresented on diagrams such as this.

8.1 *Sometimes cirrostratus associated with a jet stream will have so sharp an edge that it will throw a hard-edged shadow on the ground. This was taken by TIROS N-6 at 0909Z 16 October 1981.*

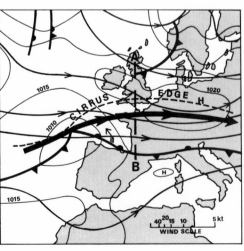

Fig. 8.1 *The surface and upper air (300 mb) situation at the time of photo 8.1. Note how the jet and the edge of the cirrus sheet roughly coincide.*

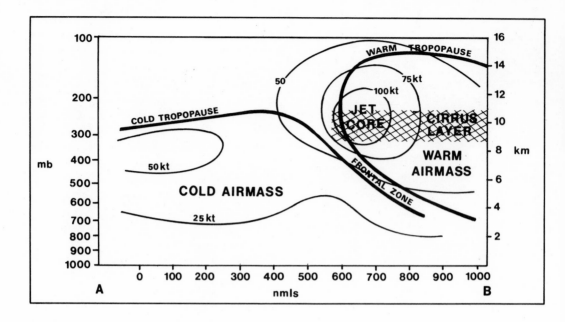

From the surface observer's point of view we see that the jet follows the edge of the cloud pretty accurately, and such edges do not form so sharply except with jets. Thus here we have another means of recognising where the jet stream blows. As you can see lower cloud through the upper, the cloud is thin and much of it may be cirrostratus. To the ground observer that means a solar halo whose radius is about a hand's span held at arm's length.

Anyone sailing in the English Channel and seeing this characteristic cirrus edge to the north could have concluded that a jet was overhead following the line of the cloud. They could then have expected that the anticyclonic weather they were enjoying would soon break down, which it subsequently did as the depression moved in across France having given gale force winds in the SW approaches.

OTHER SKIES

When fair weather is breaking down, then the characteristic cloud of fair weather –

cumulus – is often there below the encroaching high clouds. The relative directions of flight of these two cloud layers gives an accurate idea of the degree of crossing to use with the rules. This is because the Cu moves in the gradient wind which is free of frictional effects of the Earth. It therefore moves along the isobars, while the cirrus moves along the 300 mb contours (photo C.6).

As the Cu is only present because of convection currents set off by the sun, so, when the Ci becomes dense enough to cut off the sunlight substantially, the Cu fragments and eventually disappears leaving a clear vault between Earth and the high clouds. This clear vault is also characteristic of the more active frontal systems that are associated with the more intense depressions. Older fronts will exhibit cloud layers, islands and rafts below the highest clouds, and often there is Ci, Cs and As all in the higher sky at the same time while banks of Sc occupy the lower sky (photo C.7).

There was an example today as I write this. At breakfast-time the sky was covered in banners of Ci, but they were lying in

Fig. 8.2 *This shows
how the jet core was just
inside the warm airmass
and how the wind speeds
varied around it.*

many directions. The surface wind was SE. By mid-morning it was blue sky. By lunchtime it was clouding up from the west with a rapid change of cloud from Ci to As in an hour or so. By mid-afternoon it was raining, but the surface wind had not increased. The strong wind would come tomorrow. What came today were fronts driven on ahead of the surface low that was being held quasi-stationary way out to the west. The rapid onset of rain with no accompanying wind should make one think of wind to come because the strong upper winds that drive the rain clouds in over light surface winds will almost certainly appear at the surface later. 'When the rain's before the wind – then your halliards you must mind.'

It has been pointed out that sharply hooked cirrus fallstreaks indicate strong wind shear aloft and so indicate a jet stream. The other end of the scale is when fallstreaks hang down the sky as in photo C.8. They indicate no wind shear and so light winds aloft – or winds that do not change with height. In either case they preclude the development of any seriously worse or better weather except when the day appears thundery when they can be the harbingers of thundery outbreaks. In these cases the visibility is often not good.

Sometimes you can be fooled into thinking that cirrus banners are jetstream clouds. In photo C.10 it is easy to tell that these fairly fast moving banners were not running ahead of bad weather because they came from NE and the surface wind was NE also. Thus there was no development indicated and the day remained pleasant and sunny.

Cirrus need not be the only cloud in the sky. It often is when the most active warm fronts are approaching, but at first cumulus cloud will usually be present as well. Later, as the Ci increases, the Cu should tend to die out. This will leave the sky clear so that the encroaching high clouds can be seen.

In photo C.9 we see cirrus that is not prognostic of bad weather. The individual skeins are relatively short (compare photos C.1 to C.4). They are in several, widely divergent, directions. This augurs well for the night.

Sometimes once-active jet cirrus becomes divorced from the jet with which it formed and can then fool you if you do not take precautions to use several clues as to its true identity (photo C.10). In this case the clouds came in fast from the NE, but in the same direction as the surface wind. The crossed-winds rule for neutrality tells at once that there is no development in the situation revealed by this cloud despite its appearance.

SORTING OUT OBSERVATIONS OF CIRRUS

Overleaf is a chart to enable you to make more certain use of the look of skies with cirrus in them.

First: locate the main direction and length of lines in the Ci field.
Secondly: locate the heads and tails of the major individual fallstreaks.

Are the lines (banners, mare's tails, etc.) long enough to cross half or more of the sky?

If yes		*If no*	
Are they moving fast enough for you to see them in motion against the sky? (Photos C.1 to C.4.)		Are fallstreaks or other lines of Ci crossing these at wide angles (45–90°) or are the cloud elements flared out? (Photos C.8 to C.10.)	
If yes	*If no*	*If yes*	*If no*
You are looking at jet Ci. Apply crossed-winds rules to check for deterioration.	You may be looking at jet Ci but you need to make later observations. If possible confirm using crossed-winds rules.	Wind is not strong aloft and so not prognostic of developing low weather. However, can indicate risk of thundery outbreaks.	Probably indicates developing but not excessively bad weather.
If affirmative	*If negative*	*If yes*	*If no*
Expect Force 8–10 in next 12–24 hours.	Jet Ci may be old: expect a shift of wind.	Wait and make later observations.	Probably indicates developing but not excessively bad weather.

ASSESSING THE LOWER WIND

The wind direction that must be crossed to the high-level wind to indicate cyclonic or anticyclonic development is not the wind you feel. The surface wind is going to be blowing at an angle of about 15° to the gradient wind over the sea and at about 30° over the land. The angle depends on surface friction which, being greater over the land than over the sea, tends to increase the angle (fig. 8.3a).

The surface wind blows across the isobars out of high pressure into low and it may differ widely from the average values quoted above. For example when close to the centre of a travelling depression the surface wind may blow almost perpendicularly across the isobars straight into the centre of the low pressure (fig. 8.3b). The faster the low travels the more likely it is that the surface wind will do this, but even far away from a low centre the wind over the land can easily be blowing at 45° to the

isobar direction. The wide divergences from the rules will be brought about by surface inversions and low wind speeds. The daytime hours with cumulus clouds are most likely to produce average angles between the wind you assess from your wind vane, or from the vector addition of boat speed and apparent wind.

If there is low cloud, its direction of motion is the best guide to the true wind that is free of the Earth's friction. If you have a recent set of isobars for your area, either from a sketch using actuals from the shipping forecasts or (best) from the fax, then their direction is the direction of the lower wind to use with the crossed-winds rules. Otherwise you will have to take the surface wind, stand with your back to it and rotate clockwise through the requisite angle. You will then be facing the same way that the true lower wind is blowing. In any case to be out by 5° or so is not going to make a catastrophic difference to your forecast as the truly prognostic orientations are when the two winds are at right angles, and if that is 80° rather than 90° it will not matter. If the angle is about 45° or smaller, then it does matter and you must not expect the deterioration or improvement to be marked.

The above way of finding the true lower wind from the surface wind direction applies to the Northern Hemisphere. In the Southern, stand back to the wind but rotate anticlockwise through 30° or 15° depending on whether the wind is blowing over the land or the sea.

While on the subject of surface wind it will probably have become apparent from the example of the breakaway low (chapter 6) that it is the lower wind that is going to be subject to rapid change whereas the upper wind remains fairly static over much longer periods. This is particularly so when the upper wind becomes strong. All that air travelling at high speed has a great

deal of momentum and cannot be easily deflected from its path. In any case as it blows to keep low temperature on its left and high temperature on its right it only shifts as the airmasses ebb and flow.

This means that, say, you observe the flight of cirrus cloud and it looks as if it is quite strong up there. Then the cloud closes in at a lower level so your view of the high clouds is cut off. You can still assume the latter is blowing in the same direction and only slowly shifting with time. The shifts in the lower (gradient) wind will follow more or less the shifts in the surface wind although it is as well to realise that this may not always be the case.

In this context one of the most likely culprits that will make the surface wind entirely different from the gradient wind is the seabreeze. This of course occurs during the height of the day, and the early morning and late evening are not usually affected.

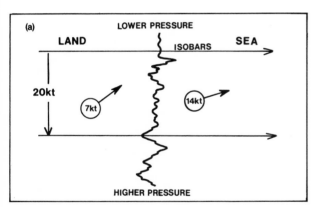
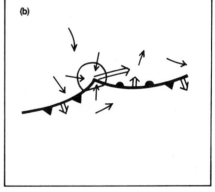

Fig. 8.3 (a) How the surface wind varies from the wind at 2000 ft. Over land the angle is on average 30° and over the sea 15° to the gradient (isobar) wind. The speed may double between land and sea. (b) When a small wave depression tracks through, the winds do not have time to obey Buys Ballot's law and blow straight into the centre.

Overnight light winds from landward are possibly nocturnal winds. These blow at their strongest (and strong means maybe 5–10 kn. at most) from midnight onwards, but are usually dead by dawn or soon after.

On land, or in close proximity to high coasts or between high islands, the surface wind will be steered by the topography and may make it impossible for you to assess the lower wind direction from the wind that you experience. Even ordinary channelways with relatively low coastlines will direct the surface wind along them in a way that might seem impossible having regard to the height of the shores. Thus when surface winds are light to moderate, care must be exercised in using the crossed-winds rules if there is any likelihood that the surface wind is being influenced by local wind-making forces of whatever kind.

Position	Advice on finding lower wind
Fully at sea or where the wind has a full sea fetch	Use surface wind and allow for 15° clockwise cant (NH) or anticlockwise cant (SH)
Coastwise	Consider time of day or night and weather conditions to see if surface wind is seabreeze or nocturnal wind. Is the coast likely to have an effect on the direction? Is the wind from the land? If so consider it a land wind and expect it to have the land cant of 30° or more
Land or with a full land fetch (land-locked waters)	Has the topography enough variation to make the wind follow it? Ignore days of convective cloud but consider evenings and mornings before sun has risen very high in the sky. At these times (and also when conditions are stable) allow for there being as much as 45° between surface wind and isobars. At normal times allow 30°

In all circumstances the flight of Cu, Sc, or St clouds will give the true wind direction.

9   FINDING THE GRADIENT WIND

The wind which is just high enough up to be clear of the effect of the surface obstacles under most circumstances is assumed to be at around 2000 ft (600 m), and for reasons given in Part Two is called the 'gradient wind'. Here, without explanation we will give the rules to be followed to find the surface wind from the gradient, the gradient from isobar spacing, etc.

The gradient wind is technically the geostrophic wind modified to take account of the curvature of the isobars. If isobars are straight or weakly curved, the gradient and the geostrophic are the same. If isobars are very strongly curved, as when close to depression centres, then the gradient is about half the geostrophic. The exact values are not really important, and fig. 9.1 gives the main useful facts. Where anticyclonic isobars are strongly curved, the gradient is stronger than geostrophic.

Using a geostrophic scale as described under that heading in Part Two on isobars which are more or less parallel and straight ('A' in fig. 8.1) find the geostrophic wind speed, g knots, and apply the following rules to find surface wind, S knots.

Over the sea with a full sea fetch (something of the order of 50 miles or more) $S = \dfrac{2\,g}{3}$

Within the lee of the land and all land-locked waters $S = \dfrac{g}{3}$

Speed of highest gusts in both cases will be g or more depending on degree of instability.

At 'A' the surface wind speed over the sea would be about 14 kn. and over the land about 7 kn., but take careful note of rules given under Inversion and under Gusts and lulls in Part Two.

At 'B', where the isobars are strongly curved cyclonically, $g = 40$ kn. and so gradient G = 20 kn. and surface wind will be as above over sea and land.

At 'C', where the isobars are relatively strongly curved anticyclonically, $g = 15$ kn. which we increase somewhat to, say, 18 kn. and then $S = 12$ kn. over the sea and 6 kn. over the land.

(Note that these are rules that have been proved statistically to apply to the situations

Fig. 9.1   *How to use a*
geostrophic scale to find
the surface wind when
given a chart whose
isobars you can rely on.

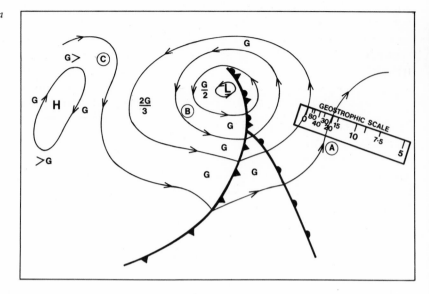

given. Time of day, time of year, topography, etc. can alter them radically. For example, at evening the direction of the gradient wind may be 45° or more different from the surface wind, etc.)

DIRECTION RULES

The surface wind blows at an average 15° to the isobar direction out of high into low over the sea and 30° over the land. This rule is more likely to be obeyed over the sea than when in the influence of the land. Gusts will tend to the direction of the isobars.

THE GRADIENT FROM THE SURFACE WIND

It is very useful when assessing the shape of the local weather map from sparse information (such as the actuals from stations in the vicinity) to be able to add your own contribution to the total. Having established that the wind you have is not bent by some

local thermal effect, you can compute the true surface wind or read it from your instruments. Let the surface wind speed be S kn. and its direction $W°$.

If you have an oceanic fetch, the gradient wind speed is $(1.5 \times S)$ kn. and its direction is $(W + 15)°$ where + indicates clockwise (NH). If you have a land fetch, the gradient speed is $(3 \times S)$ kn. and its direction is $(W + 30)°$. For example, you have a surface wind speed when you are off a lee shore of 200°/12 kn. Thus the gradient (for an oceanic fetch) will be 215°/18 kn.

Off a windward shore this same measured surface direction and speed will amount to 230°/36 kn. You may drop this latter speed a little because the wind will have become free of surface friction over the sea and you can drop it again when the wind from the land is unstable with gusts and lulls.

If you know or suspect that you are under strongly curved cyclonic isobars, remember that the surface wind will be the above fractions of a gradient wind that can be as much as half of the value you would measure from the isobar spacing using a geostrophic scale. Thus, having applied the above rules to find the gradient, double that very near low centres and maybe take one-and-a-half times it further away from the centre or where you appear to be in a trough.

THE SITUATION AT 1800 GMT 11 AUGUST 1979

The weather map of Britain and the nearer continent (fig. 9.2) has been drawn up with isobars at 1 mb intervals to throw up the places where the speed and direction rules apply and where they do not. To take specific examples:

S is Scilly Isles. Direction fits the rules very well, but speed is just a little higher than would be expected for an oceanic place.

P is Plymouth and the NW wind of 10 kn.

is due to flow over the high ground inland and then down the Tamar valley.

H is Hurn Airport and the SE wind is seabreeze which is typical of the south coast of England from here down into Kent.

B is Bristol (Filton) and its 15 kn. from the Bristol Channel is well above that to be expected from the gradient. This is due to (i) help from seabreeze forces, and (ii) funnelling up the constrictions of the Channel.

U is Ushant off the Brest Peninsula. Note the way the station inland takes a cant across the isobars compared with the oceanic directions.

J is Jersey, and together with St Malo has an oceanic 15 kn. while the coastal stations all take a cant for the wind to blow parallel to the coast. This is an example of steering which occurs most often along N-facing coasts.

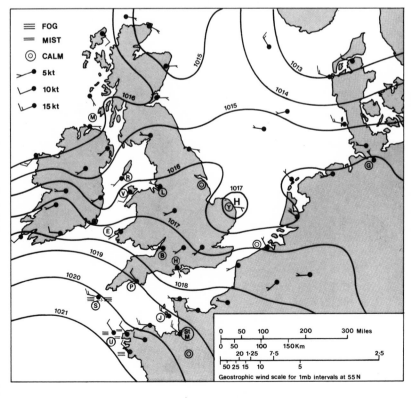

Fig. 9.2 *A summer situation to illustrate the things that can alter the wind speed and direction.*

O is Ostend, and all the way up the coast of the Low Countries the winds are sea-breeze directed as is the wind at G, which is Hamburg aided by the lie of the river estuary. Similarly on the Danish coast the 20 kn. winds are above gradient and are seabreeze assisted.

Y is Yarmouth (Gorleston), and all up the east coast of England and Scotland the winds are anti-gradient in direction because of the seabreeze.

Winds in the Irish Sea are obeying the gradient but L is Liverpool (Speke) and the wind there is directed by the seabreeze and by the lie of the Mersey.

V and R are Valley (Anglesea) and Ronaldsway (Isle of Man) and having no real land influences are running fairly true to the gradient.

As Ireland was largely cloudy there were no seabreeze effects to consider and so most winds are what you might expect from the gradient – except for M which is Malin Head where the wind is light easterly and not apparently conforming to any obvious trend. You do get some like that when the wind is light. It is the situation covered by the blanket phrase 'Winds, light, variable'.

SUMMARY OF EFFECTS

This actual example throws up questions to be answered when comparing winds at stations with each other or your own wind.

(a)   Wind slightly different from that to be expected: could be lie of the land or of the coast; it could be steering along coasts, especially high coasts. It could be that you do not know the isobar direction sufficiently accurately.

(b)   Wind widely different from expected: seabreeze at work by day or nocturnal wind by night. Former on-shore the latter off-shore. Flow into estuaries or channels. Flow due to mountains near to or not so near to the coast, e.g. mistral in Gulf of Lions or bora in the Adriatic also flow from the Pyrenees at places like Biarritz. Flow into local heat lows over land on unseasonably hot days – also out of local highs over waters such as the North Sea or the Baltic in middle of such days. Flow from bodies of locally cooler water to warmer water, e.g. across Gulf Stream boundaries or even from cool water off tidal harbours into warm tidal ebbs or conversely from cold ebb waters to relatively warm surroundings (see Ref. 16). Flow into or out of thunder-storm areas (usually over land) which may be too far away to detect by lightning or thunder. Monsoonal effects such as occur in the English Channel and up the coast of the Low Countries and into the Baltic in late spring and summer as well as the more celebrated monsoons of hot countries.

10   FRONTAL SYSTEMS

The examples of the frontal systems over America which appear on charts in chapter 7 show how complex the analysis of such systems can be. The mariner without charts to help him has to assess what is happening from the look of the sky, the way the wind is shifting and the way the barometer is behaving. Yet real frontal systems will diverge from the textbook ideas in many ways and on many occasions. When the winds blow hard, then, within reason, the way the weather shapes follows the textbook ideas of how lows and their fronts behave.

For example take the weather map of North America for a day in October 1981 and look at the low off the East Coast of the USA (fig. 10.1). Apart from the direction of orientation of the warm sector, this looks just like the diagrams in the textbooks. There is a warm front moving ahead of a cold front and for part of its length the latter has become occluded while the low centre has re-formed around the point of occlusion. There is cirrus cloud to be seen in skies that are clouding up ahead of where the warm frontal rain and drizzle is to be found. There is rain around the cold front, but some of it is in the warm sector as allowed for in the conveyor-belt model (see Part Two, Depressions) and there is the odd thunderstorm in the trough that sticks out southward from the low centre. Further, searching the chart for winds that are 25 kn. or stronger the only ones are around this low. So under its circulation you would recognise a textbook situation. What you would not realise is that the warm front is on a collision course with a cold front moving slowly in the opposite direction!

There are quite a few showers being set off by the cold frontal trough which is part of a complex low over Greenland. People from Virginia to Maine who were looking at their sky would take the Ci as a sign that a warm front or occlusion was on its way. There were no showers from the cold frontal trough down the coastal belt and therefore little sign that there was a cold front stretched down the Appalachian Mountains.

Yet when these two fronts meet up they will probably form one system which to the observer will be detected as two very close

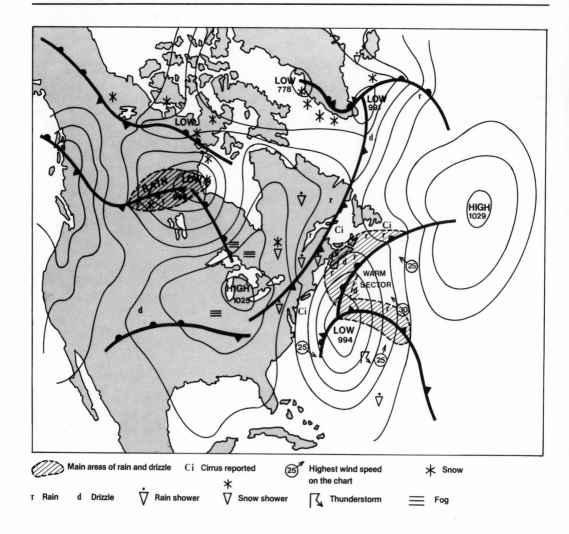

| | Main areas of rain and drizzle | Ci Cirrus reported | 25 Highest wind speed on the chart | * Snow |
| r Rain | d Drizzle | V̇ Rain shower | V Snow shower | Thunderstorm | Fog |

Fig. 10.1 *Many fronts do not follow textbook rules. So you have to read the charts as they appear and apply your knowledge of fronts to assess the likely wind and weather.*

systems. This can happen quite often – that given as a single front on the charts is, in reality, a multiple system. I have experienced several of these and I remember one where there was a rather rapid build-up of frontal cloud which lowered to a dark cloud line with a little rain and it then passed. This was followed by a lightening of the sky for a while before a second frontal line of low trailing cloud (virga) passed, only for the process to be repeated once again before the sky finally broke.

Multiple fronts may not be as close to one another as that. The transition from the warm air in a warm sector may be accomplished in two or even three distinct phases under each of which the wind veers (NH) partially to encompass the whole final wind-shift. The whole process may take several hours or as much as half a day or more.

The low near Hudson Bay is relatively dry as it is only producing rain around the cold front and very little if any around the warm front. This illustrates the fact that while the textbook ana-cold front does not rain until the frontal line (as drawn on the weather map) passes, in practice older kata fronts can have precipitation ahead of them whatever the textbooks may say. These are generally older frontal systems, but they can rejuvenate by the process called fronto-genesis just as quite virile fronts can be damped out by the process called frontolysis. Generally frontogenesis comes about by the injection of a blast of cold air which does not have to be noticeable in the surface observations whereas frontolysis is nearly always produced by air subsiding over the front.

When I was a forecaster we often used to keep fronts going on our charts even after they had been officially dropped as of no further consequence, and it was amazing how often doing that helped to explain the sudden increase of cloud or an unexpected shower of rain.

Thus when fronts like the one over the central United States are retained they may not amount to anything other than an increase in cloudiness, maybe the smallest amount of rain or drizzle and perhaps a little wind-shift that could be of use on the next leg of a long beat.

Because this is October the frontal systems over Northern Canada and Greenland are accompanied by snow, and snow from fronts commences sooner than rain would. This is because a lot of evaporation goes on from the first small falling raindrops. So at first the rain from high warm frontal clouds may not reach the ground, but when the freezing level is on the surface or below, everything that falls reaches the ground. As it then hangs about and is inconvenient, it is noticeable in a way that rain is not. A shower of rain is soon forgotten but a shower of snow is a cause for worried phone calls, so snow will often be forecast just to be on the safe side when the chances of it happening are slim.

Enough may have been said to convince the reader that fronts may differ widely from the textbook descriptions of them. Yet when all is said and done the facts remain:

Fronts bring rain and snow, etc.
Fronts bring veering wind-shifts (NH)
  (backing in SH).
The weather type changes when fronts
  pass.

We will now describe the fronts them-selves and the inferences about wind-shifts that can be drawn from observations.

11 ABOUT WARM FRONTS AND OCCLUSIONS

The signs of warm fronts (or occlusions) approaching start with the appearance of cirrus which extends into cirrostratus with haloes about sun or moon. These two cloud types following one another allied to crossed winds for cyclonic development make it pretty certain that a front is on its way.

Forecasts will give an indication of when rain from the front is expected, but before that the wind will have to have made certain changes depending on what it was before the cirrus appeared. The example of fig. 8.1 shows how the cirrus and the jet can invade an anticyclone or ridge where the surface wind will be light and so very subject to modification by thermal winds such as seabreezes. However, the invasion of the sky by a substantial cirrus layer can cut off enough of the sun's heat to preclude seabreeze activity or at least curtail it. Even so it is important to remember that had the example been in the late spring or the summer instead of the autumn the absence of cloud would have seen seabreezes setting in early in the forenoon wherever they could.

Now assuming that the sun has shone for the forenoon and coastwise there is a seabreeze current blowing on-shore, the sharply cut cirrus veil means that you must have a jet to contend with even though you cannot use the surface wind direction to assess the development of the situation. Even without a formal forecast you realise that the cirrus is from an active front and so you expect the wind to pick up eventually from the S or possibly SE.

Over the Brest peninsula and the south-west corner of England this S wind has already begun to pull in (fig. 8.1) by 1200Z, but over central and south-east England, Wales, Ireland, and the Channel and North Sea coasts of France, Belgium, Holland and Germany there is very little gradient – if any. In summer, seabreezes would blow over all these coasts wherever the sun was out.

The satellite picture (photo 8.1) indicates very little low cloud although as the time is breakfast-time it is possible that Cu will develop and allow the gradient wind, such as it is, to be assessed. The seabreeze will blow under the Cu, but subsiding air over any coastal belt will clear that region of cloud anyway.

Thus this example illustrates very well some important points about use of the crossed-winds rules and shows that while the surface wind is almost nil the wind may still be jet speed at 30 000 ft. If it is jet speed up there now, it is a sign to check whether the forecast is going for strong wind to follow some hours later.

The gradient wind ahead of travelling depressions is very often W in the ridge that precedes the low. Thus in the majority of cases the wind will have to back (shift anticlockwise) as the warm front approaches. Backing winds are the hand-maidens of approaching troughs whether they be frontal or non-frontal. Whenever the wind backs you need to ask yourself 'Is this the first sign of a developing trough situation?' In snow situations it is very noticeable that before another snow-belt comes along the wind backs ahead of it. That means that it will veer behind it unless there has been some permanent change in the direction of the isobars. The same goes for rainy troughs.

In our case we have a frontal trough approaching the Channel area, but what wind there was in the North Sea would be W. As the low approached, this W wind would have to fall light and then back into the SE. In the Channel itself there would be no such change: in fact the wind along the central south coast of England would be E and so would veer as it picked up into an SE wind. Thus there are occasions when the rule that 'Wind backs before an approaching warm front or occlusion' is broken. Anyway when the developing gradient sweeps away a seabreeze there is no relation between the breeze direction (which depends on the lie of the coast) and the gradient direction.

Yet having said this the rule that winds back as pressure falls is a meteorological truism and will be evident on very many more occasions than those when something else happens.

When the wind will increase is always a problem, and what its direction will be is even more so. Frontal rain can be carried forward on the back of strong upper winds and will break out before any major increase in wind has occurred. This should make one think of stronger surface wind to come, but not necessarily from a direction backed to the present regime of lighter wind. Stronger wind will also produce an increase in low cloud that can have a lowering effect on crew morale on many occasions. This cloud is turbulence set off by a combination of the wind increase and the high humidity.

The second message in the onset of a warm front is the thought that there is warmer, and therefore more humid, air behind it. There is also a veer of wind of some kind to come as it passes, but this veer may not be sharp and can occupy an hour or more depending on how old the front is and how far it has come over land before it gets to you.

When you have a chart of some kind to help you, you can move on a warm front from its last position remembering that the front tends to move at two-thirds of the speed of the gradient wind behind it. You have to measure the gradient using a geostrophic scale which may be on the chart itself or you have to work from a fixed blank chart whose scale is known and for which you have already produced a scale as explained on page 183. If the front lies in a region of the isobars that are very strongly curved, then halve the geostrophic speed you measure. If the isobars are only gently curved, the gradient is the same as the geostrophic.

If, in your estimation, the front is pretty close but there are no actual signs of its passage on the windward horizon, a single actual observation can give you the information you seek. For example in fig. 11.1 you are at X and have a southerly wind of about 25 kn. The isobars over you can be drawn by remembering that the

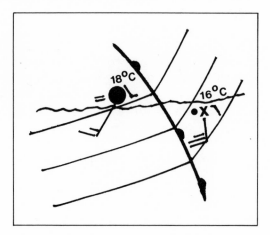

Fig. 11.1   *Where you are (at X) you know the exact state of the weather and wind. If you already know a front is   somewhere near, one other actual observation can tell you more nearly when to expect it and its wind-shift.*

gradient wind is veered by about 15° to the surface wind direction and that its speed will be a third up on the surface wind. So you assume the gradient is something over 30 kn.

A coastal station to windward gives its wind speed as 15 kn. from SW, with mist and a barometer that was falling but is now steady. If you also know the air temperature and it is significantly higher than yours, then all these clues point to the front being through there. If you also have the dew-point temperature and it is close to air temperature, this is another clue on the side of the station being in the warm sector.

A wind of 15 kn. at a station known to be on land means 20 kn. or more at sea and the wind will be backed by some 30° to the isobars. Thus the isobar direction in the warm sector will be known and their spacing also, which should conform to the sketch. If it does not, then something odd is happening and you have not got a textbook warm front on your hands.

If the wind speed at sea is 20 kn. in the

warm sector, then the gradient is 27 or so knots and the warm front moves at two-thirds of this, i.e. 18 kn. All these figures are rough so you will probably time the front's arrival using a speed nearer to 20 kn. to be on the safe side.

The direction of the isobars in the warm sector is usually the same as the direction in which the low centre is moving so you have another useful piece of information from your sketch based on your knowledge of how isobars and fronts tie together and on your own and one other neighbouring observation.

Those with fax who want to know the most likely movement of a low centre can use the direction of the contours of the 500 mb surface above it as it has been proved that lows tend to move with the wind at this level.

While they are less common, waves form on warm fronts much as they do on cold fronts. Such waves produce a more than expected deterioration in weather elements. They induce winds to lighten when they should be steady or increasing, and they swing the direction round to conform to their own local low-pressure centre. Any lightening of the wind as a warm front approaches should be viewed as an indication that a wave may be the reason. Do not forget that once the wave has rippled up the front the wind will come in just as before – maybe stronger. Waves tend to delay the passage of fronts and so make nonsense of forecasts of clearance.

OCCLUDED FRONTS

Occluded fronts occur because the cold front moves faster than the warm front in a wave depression and so with time it over-takes it. All the time the low is an open wave it will continue to deepen. Its centre will also lie to the south of its attendant jet, but as time proceeds the surface centre slides under the jet. This is a signal for the low to begin the process of 'filling', i.e. its central pressure stops falling and will soon begin to rise. It is also the signal for the occlusion process to start, and in general the point of occlusion on the weather map slides down the fronts keeping itself more or less under the jet above it. The low will track through to the north of the jet (south in SH) as the occlusion process proceeds, and so low centres to the north of the main jet stream axis indicate older, filling systems. If they have fronts that are still recognisable, then some or all of the frontal system will be occlusion.

There are two kinds of occlusion:

(a) warm occlusions occur when the air behind the front is relatively warmer than that ahead;

(b) cold occlusions occur when the air behind the front is colder than that ahead.

The latter is most often seen in textbooks, but it is the former that very often holds the stage in Europe.

The signs of the occlusion approaching include:

(a) no true jet cirrus as this lies on the equatorial side of the jet;

(b) rapid change from Ci to Cs to As, often with gaps and holes in the cloud sheets. With older occlusions all three cloud types plus Sc may be in the sky at the same time. Obviously such a short forecast means soon past (photos 11.1, C.7 and C.13).

(c) when the break in the frontal rain appears it is not a true one. The more continuous rain will often give way to showers mixed with continuous rain. This follows because warm frontal rain is replaced by cold frontal rain without any warm air at the surface. The showery conditions may set in before the occlusion (as represented by the line on the weather map) has reached you.

As with all fronts they only obey the textbook ideas when they are parts of well-developed depressions, and quite often a weather map will show occlusions that have long lost any contact with jet streams and depression centres with which they formed.

11.1   *Cloud can be at many different heights, and sunset is the best time to see which layer is below which. This is a typical sky ahead of a coming occlusion.*

Old occlusions can loop down into the centres or highs and then you can only expect that the line on the chart represents in actual fact a more than expected sky of medium and high cloud with perhaps some more extensive low cloud to go with them. Nothing that can be recognised as a frontal passage occurs at the ground although sometimes a weak shift of wind is discernible.

In effect the occlusion will not be vicious in the way that the ana-cold front is vicious, nor will it be as virile as the ana-warm front. It may indeed amount to a very poor apology for a front.

12 ABOUT COLD FRONTS

Cold fronts are warm fronts in reverse. Their worst weather is at the head of the front, i.e. where the frontal line is on the weather map. Here we get heavy showers, squalls and an often sharp veer of wind. Behind this rough leading edge expect the rain to tail away in direct contrast to the warm front where the rain starts light and increases in intensity. Mesoscale precipitation areas (MPAs) can induce periods of more intense showery-type rain and consequent gusts to go with them mixed with the continuous rain.

The problem with forecasting cold fronts from the surface is that they often hide their approach behind a veil of low cloud. When they do not and the sky is more or less clear, look for false-cirrus anvils and generally high rounded cloud tops emerging out of a more general assemblage of lower cloud. Expect the cold front to come from the left of the surface wind direction, e.g. from W or NW when the surface wind is around SW (NH): photo 12.1.

In practice, cold fronts can be multiple, each one lowering the temperature slightly as it passes. Sometimes a change from mT to mP air is accomplished only when three fronts have succeeded one another. Let's look at an example of what can happen.

On the afternoon of Sunday 14 July 1985 the wind had been southerly for much of the day and it was hot and humid with the temperatures in the 80s. A cold front came down on us around tea-time with a crop of thunderstorms. The wind veered sharply NW for a time and there were odd-looking motions in the clouds as the low cloud characteristically came from NW (the wind to expect after the front has passed) while the higher cloud continued to stream from around south.

The temperature fell by about 8°F and there was a short-lived clearance after which the wind went back SW with gathering cloud. All this looked like a second front to come and after an early-evening cloudbelt had gone and the sky finally cleared I knew that a second front had passed.

Sometimes some hours behind a cold front there is a trough and this may look like another cold front (photo C.18). However, troughs will not usually lower the temperature when they pass whereas cold

12.1   *A cold front approaches. Ignore the outriding cumulus and concentrate on the deep clouds that must be under the cirrus. That is where the big squalls are.*

fronts will. The typical weather in these airmass troughs is showers which appear over the windward horizon stretched across the wind direction. With them may be more-continuous rain, and it will be very difficult without help from an official source to make up your mind that this is not in fact another cold front.

Also upper troughs can feed a veil of high cloud in behind the retreating cold front and make it look as if another deterioration is on the way. However, you can differentiate between this, largely harmless, cloud build-up and the cirrus of a real secondary depression by using the crossed-winds rules. If there is no very obvious angle between upper and lower winds, then all the upper cloud will do is damp out any showers. If the surface wind backs and crosses the high cloud, go for a blow – and maybe a nasty one.

COLD-FRONT TACTICS

When a cold front is forecast you want to get the veer as it passes correctly to gain maximum advantage, and also to meet it on the starboard tack. (It is a back in the SH and you will meet it best on port tack.) Here is a checklist on cold fronts.

Characteristics

Ana-cold fronts (ACF) are sharp with temporarily strong squally winds, heavy rain and/or hail plus the chance of passing thunder. Seas are confused, as typically a NW wind replaces a SW one and does so in a matter of minutes. Ana fronts are contained in the circulation of depressions in the first half of their life-cycle – that is until the occlusion process has begun in earnest. Passage over land and especially hills often spreads the wind-shift zone so that instead of a single sudden veer the total shift is dispersed over a period measured in tens of minutes or even as much as an hour. See table 12.1.

Subsidence of air from above leads to kata-cold fronts (KCF) and if only light rain is forecast it is likely that a KCF is responsible.

Table 12.1   Characteristics of an ana-cold-front passage

Conditions before	Conditions during passage	Conditions afterwards
Warm, moist mT air. Poor visibility or even fog. Many other combinations of conditions possible in a warm sector. However, cloud islands at several levels likely. Warm and humid usually but can be warm and dry. Sometimes much very low cloud from which drizzle or light rain falls	Cloud wall showing turbulent motions in the clouds when close. Expect wind shift under leading edge or maybe just ahead. Very often there is a clear break in what has been a very cloudy airstream when cold front is imminent. Allow for 30+ knots temporarily in squalls	Rain may fall for as little as an hour or maybe 3 to 4 hours. Clearance to mainly clear skies (photo C.15). Wind may increase. It will now come from a direction veered to dn. before the front passed. Expect showers – if you do not get any and air seems to be stabilising, expect another low

MEANS OF TIMING A COLD FRONT (CF)

The best guide is the forecast charts from a fax machine. Even so, minutes matter in yacht racing so monitor actual reports from stations upwind. Look for any or all of the following between two observations at sites you know must be close to the CF position.

Present weather – cloudy or fair in *past* weather (see page 180) and showers or rain from 8/8 cover in *present* weather. With sharp CF, *past* weather may be showers while *present* is rain

Shift of wind – a veer which may occupy 90° or more (back in SH)

Wind speed – 20–40 kn. in the heavy rain or showers, possibly less in the lighter rain behind the leading edge squall

Temperature – fall of several degrees in many cases

Barograph trace – steady then rising or falling then rising; pressure higher than three hours ago

Visibility – increase except if heavy showers or rain occurring at time of observation

(Remember that observations are taken at met. stations about ten minutes to the hour)

Occasionally the actuals given with shipping forecasts can coincide with the need to locate a cold front more precisely, but if you have fax the last reliable chart showing the CF can be used as a basis for extrapolating the position of the front forward. The 12- or 24-hour-ahead forecast chart will give where it is thought it will be.

The rule most often used is that the CF moves with the speed of the component of the wind behind it that is directed perpendicular to the front. You need a geostrophic scale for your charts to find the true gradient wind speed. Otherwise you can use radio to ascertain if the front has passed a local coastguard or coast radio station.

Preambles to shipping forecasts can give a good initial position for the front, and the surface wind at stations known to be behind it can be scaled up to give gradient speed. (See page 60.) The front can then be roughly moved on and an estimated time of arrival established for it. The watch can be told to keep a weather eye out for it.

Weather men are always testing their own ability to get it right, and it is worth noting that, in computer-aided forecasts for 24 hours ahead on timing cold fronts during the winter of 1983/84, by far the greatest number of errors were made in assessing the speed of cold fronts. The error is almost always too fast, and this can be borne in mind when looking at forecast charts or when believing forecast positions given in shipping forecasts, etc. It is as well to give the actual figures for the period November 1983–February 1984 (from the Meteorological Office Annual Report 1984) (table 12.2).

The average speed of cold fronts is round 25–30 kn. and so two-thirds of the data in table 12.2 were within two hours of being right. Now two hours is a very long time at sea and so we need to refine the estimated time of arrival via the methods outlined above.

FOLLOWING WEATHER

Is this the last of a line of lows, or is another one on the way? Without charts to tell you watch the motion of Ci cloud along the rear of the CF as it clears (photo C.15). If the Ci moves roughly at 90° to wind near the surface, but from its right, e.g. high cloud from SW while surface wind is from NW, anticyclonic development is taking place and will follow the low in. If the upper and lower winds are more or less in the same direction, then anticipate that another low or maybe a trough is on the way.

The cold air behind a CF should produce showers, or at least large Cu clouds that look close to producing showers. For a fine settled spell these showers together with a moderate to fresh wind should persist for a day or two, gradually reverting to fair conditions with small Cu (photo C.17). Winds should lighten. If they do not, then the most likely cause is that the low has stuck to the east of you while the high has built towards you and tightened the gradient over you.

Troughs, both initiated from the surface and engendered at altitude (upper troughs), often follow in the wake of cold fronts. The

Table 12.2

Error in position of front (nautical miles)	Cold	Warm	Occlusion	All
Forecast too fast				
200 or more	0	0	0	0
150–200	1	1	0	2
100–150	3	2	3	8
50–100	11	4	8	23
50 or less	38	27	23	88
Forecast too slow				
50–100	3	1	0	4
100–150	1	1	1	3
150+	0	0	1	1

principle of exclusivity (page 86) says that both before and after such troughs the air will be more stable to make up for the instability in the trough itself. This way there are variations in the quantity of showers. On the satellite pictures the intensely showery airstream will look like a more or less homogeneous flock of sheep being driven to your market down the drovers' way of the isobars. This way you can often see what possible respite there may be from them. You can get a glimpse of that from the TV or better get the latest nephanalysis on the fax.

13 CYCLONIC WINDS AND WEATHER

GENERAL CONSIDERATIONS

These pages are concerned with wind and weather under generally cyclonically curved isobars. In such situations some periods with slightly anticyclonic curvature come along when the generally poor weather improves somewhat. For example, a few breaks may occur in the otherwise total cloud cover, or precipitation may die out whereas before it was more or less continuous (fig. 13.1). There is usually a neighbouring parent low which may be quasi-stationary and often complex in form, consisting of two or more centres sprawled over a very large area. The degree of general movement is often small, but there can nevertheless be considerable variation in wind direction and speed and weather from day to day and hour to hour.

Here we cover the weather of less virile cyclonic systems than are covered on page 70. Also the basic weather patterns are not considered to be very mobile here whereas they are in table 13.1 (Depression coming in). Note that the shipping forecast term of 'cyclonic' can mean wind-shift patterns as given on page 152 and, more rarely, as given here. On the whole we are talking about the weather and wind under the circulation of lows that have stuck near the area of interest.

Without fax

FORECAST SOURCES
Domestic radio for land areas will usually be rather vague about the timing of weather elements. Rain that occurs intermittently may be described under the collective head of 'showers'. Often no indication can be given as to when periods of rain will arrive or how long they will last; when clouds will break or close in; what the wind will be other than a vague suggestion as to direction 'at first' and 'later'.

Shipping forecasts will usually say 'cyclonic variable' when a travelling low is going to cross a sea area, whereas in the case considered here they may well indicate more or less persistent conditions with terms such as rain, snow showers, etc. It is up to the mariner to make up his mind from the wind-shift pattern where the low is going to track compared with his own position (that is, if it tracks anywhere at all). *Navtex* will not be any more helpful than the shipping forecast.

Coast radio stations or *coastguards* can give rather more precise indication of wind direction over limited parts of the coastal waters.

Marineline telephone will usually be as vague about the weather as domestic radio, but may give a better view of the wind.

TV Through timelapse presentation of weather maps with satellite back-up a better view of trends in the onset of troughs and ridges may be had. For best results the pause-and-draw method using a video recorder is necessary (page 184).

Viewdata is not likely to be any more helpful over wind trends than domestic radio.

Your own observations are of paramount importance here for the mesoscale and microscale changes that will affect you.

MAIN CONSIDERATIONS
Cyclonic weather is cloudy. It is associated with lifting air, and every break in the cloudiness is threatened by re-invasion by cloud and precipitation. Wind may be anything from light variable to strong to gale. However, for the most part the poorer periods come in zones (troughs) preceded and followed by pleasanter periods.

LOW POSITION OR TRACK
The position of the quasi-stationary low that is the main cause of the problem will have been evident for days (possibly) before now. A major position for Europe is south of Iceland, but such a position means other centres and fronts swinging up across Atlantic Europe and leading to a long period of changeable weather.

POSSIBLE VARIATIONS IN SITUATION
Some quite delightful days come along under mainly cyclonic conditions, but they are the exception. It may become warm to

hot for the time of year, and the situation is always threatened by further deteriorations. Winds may become almost calm when the low sprawls across the region, and fog is a distinct possibility whenever the cloud clears overnight. When caught in the doldrums between the centres of a complex area of low pressure there is nothing to be done but sail to the wind you have. It is often impossible to say where the wind will come from later as the centres crawl around from one place to another. The longer-range forecasts will give an idea of when this sluggish situation is likely to give way to a more mobile pattern.

When a quasi-stationary low is dominant and refuses to fill up, the growth of pressure on its periphery will lead to an increase in the gradient. Under such conditions winds may grow to strong to gale, and can continue that way for a considerable period with very little change of direction.

REASONS FOR SEEKING INFORMATION
In cyclonic situations the weather is never static. Unless every avenue of information is explored, the wind-shifts of the next few hours will become a closed book.

With fax
Gridding the surface chart with the 300 or even 500 mb chart for that same time will indicate whether the surface low can move or not and allow you to follow the development of the situation. For immediate purposes obtain each three-hourly 'plotted points' chart and draw up the isobars over your area taking care to follow the wiggles as much as possible. It often helps to draw the isobars at 1 mb intervals to see how the minor troughs and ridges are developing over you. Follow them from chart to chart noting when they are persistent or transitory. This way you may detect the next mesoscale wind shift.

Expect lows routed towards the edges of the main quasi-stationary low to be drawn into it, to reinforce it or at least to add to its sum total of cyclonic vorticity. Thus expect the individual low now coming in to disappear tomorrow, maybe to be replaced by another one hungry to be gobbled up by big brother.

A typical situation is illustrated in fig. 13.1. At position such as A, the low may have become slow-moving because it has failed to move a persistent high and then winds become strong or even gale. Look back down the isobars to where the air is coming from to detect degree of cloudiness and how damp the air is. Moving slightly towards the high may radically alter the character of the weather.

At B, there is fairly strong curvature of the isobars and we must expect intermittent rain and drizzle or showers, and thicker

cloud and more of it than elsewhere. However, if B should be fed from a 'dry' area such as a continental landmass, then cloud can break to hazy blue skies.

At C there is a weak ridge where clouds are likely to break and conditions generally improve, and at D winds will be very light, and persistent rain may fall from leaden skies.

Do not forget that here, where the isobars are most strongly curved, the wind may well blow almost directly across the isobars into low pressure.

DEPRESSION COMING IN

General situation
It is assumed that at this time you are still under the influence of the ridge of high pressure that precedes the low. The low is a polar-front depression and is travelling in some easterly direction.

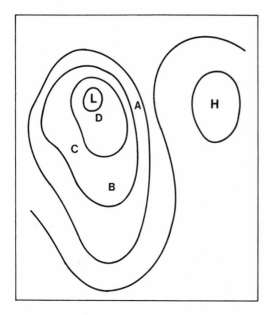

Fig. 13.1   *The way the isobars curve is indicative of the weather that goes with them. It depends on whether the isobars are cyclonically or anticyclonically curved.*

Without fax

FORECAST SOURCES
(a)   Domestic radio for land areas (which will indicate when rain belts are expected, so giving some timing on the arrival of fronts, and will by inference indicate winds of Force 6+ at sea when described as fresh to strong for land, etc.).

(b)   'Gale' stations like BBC Radio 4 on 1500 m and Allouis (France) on domestic radio shipping forecasts which give general inference and are the best guide to wind speed at sea, visibility, etc.

(c)   Viewdata systems give latest forecast update.

(d)   Television (time-lapse presentations of progress of low and its fronts if taken on video and freeze-framed can be a valuable substitute for fax. Satellite pictures may be helpful).

(e)   VHF to coast radio stations for latest

forecast and gale summary.

(f) Marine telephone forecasts may not give much synoptic information (needs backing up with TV charts).

(g) Your own sky observation, e.g. distant storm swell detected under the seaway, etc.

General considerations
Look for: cirrus invading high sky; wind showing some tendency to increase and back towards southerly quadrants from more westerly ones; barometer beginning to fall; possibly exceptional visibility. Present weather assumed generally fair with Cu or Sc clouds, but sometimes there can be low stratus and/or fog (rare).

Low track and intensity determination
Use ideas under Cyclonic in Part Two to gain an idea of what the depression's track is compared with your own position. The further north in temperate latitudes the greater chance that the low will track south of you. Generally in Atlantic Europe lows tend to curve to the north-east, but they sometimes do the opposite.

Some idea of intensity can be gained from Ci observation. Jet stream speed and sight of true jet cirrus indicate possible severe gale in outlook. If sky remains covered in Sc or similar cloud layer, then low is not likely to be very intense. When visible, use the orientation of Ci banners or fallstreaks from individual Ci clouds to locate direction of centre.

Progressive observations
If low is travelling and acting normally we must expect:

First sky signs – Ci rapidly invading high sky with progressive build-up to much of sky covered. With jets, polar edge of Ci is often cut-off into clear sky (very noticeable). Bar falling slowly as yet.

Wind light to moderate. See photos C.1–C.4.

Second sky sign – Ci gives way to Cs with halo about sun or moon (photo C.9). With virile systems there is progressive blending of one cloud type into the next. Bar now falling more steeply. Wind backing or backed into equatorial quadrants – some increase.

Third sky sign – Cs undercut by darker and thickening As banks. Sun begins to be lost (photo C.12). The steady onset of these three types gives confidence that the coming front is an ana warm front and therefore depression is on the higher side of average intensity. Bar could now be falling steeply and wind rising to Force 5–6 from equatorial quadrants.

Fourth sky sign – Dark, largely featureless As continues to thicken and then rain starts. In rain, pannus forms and spreads to cover whole sky (photo C.14). Cloud type now Ns with St pan below. Bar still falling rapidly.

Warm-front passage – Look for trailing virga with lightness behind. Wind veers. Bar kicks. Rain ceases. Sky lifts – possibly broken for a short while. Airmass changes to mT so there are fog and stratus risks.

Reasons for seeking information
Depressions bring strong to gale winds on many occasions. Fair conditions with good visibility deteriorate to low stratus with moderate (possibly heavy) precipitation. Then after warm front passes, fog risk goes up significantly. Severe gales which become survival conditions for many must be forecast and recipients advised several hours in advance, so that shelter or open sea can be sought.

With fax

YACHT'S INITIAL POSITION SIMILAR TO A IN FIG. 9.1
The latest actual surface chart will show the

Table 13.1   Depression coming in: wind-shift possibilities

Gradient direction	High cloud	Barometer
SE – often not above moderate and can be light	Advancing from SW	Falling or tending to fall
SE – any speed but most likely to be light to moderate	From S or SE	No real sign of fall
SE – often quite light	From around NW	Has fallen, now steady
S – light to moderate	From W or NW	Falling slowly
S – strong	From W or hardly detectable movement	Falling or steady
S – moderate, increasing	From W rapidly increasing	Fall slow as yet – expect steeper fall
SW – backing from W	From NW – hooked Ci and/or jet Ci. If Cs you are later in the cyclonic cloud sequence	Definite and purposeful fall that should increase
SW – steady for many hours	From W or SW	Slight changes without much purpose
W	From W or NW at easily noticeable speed	Falling

Expect	Later wind should:	Wind was:
– wind to back no further and to even veer S a little when the wind freshens	– increase, veering S or even SW but possibly not the latter until the warm front or occlusion has passed	– W or SW under a collapsing ridge. Now backed to SE under increasing upper cloud
– wind to stay where it is and maybe not change speed much. If wind backs, then consider a wave low in the offing	– increase somewhat but barometer must fall a little first. If backs E, then low will track south of you. If it is a wave low, then you may be in its path so expect cyclonic changes	– probably much the same as now. However, whatever the previous direction was, a 'no-change' orientation now of upper and lower wind should be carefully monitored with time to see what changes may be in store
– low to be tracking south-east to south of you. Could be a cold front wave	– not change substantially until the cloud at upper levels tends to clear. Then it will probably back through E towards N. A wave generally passes in a few hours	– probably more southerly but could have been almost any direction before present gradient took over
– low may be slow to advance or a weak feature. Wind may be backing SE in which case expect increase soon	– maintain increase and then veer back to S and later SW: may even go W as trough-line passes with some precipitation	– most probably much the same as now but lighter
– expect stronger wind yet and some veering towards SW as it does so	– increase as precipitation comes. Wind may then also veer a point or so before a warm front or occlusion passes. Winds could get to gale if barometer falls rapidly. Deterioration may be short-lived	– probably much the same direction but lighter
– wind to back further before it increases, maybe to gale. Then expect some veering	– veer across frontal trough lines. Could be squally	– some direction other than S but shifted or picked up positively from S
– wind to back further, maybe as far as SE. If not, should grow to strong to gale before many hours are over	– be as above. Can be some backing immediately ahead of frontal troughs. Wind should get stronger then. Less variable when troughs have passed	– NW or W light to moderate normally but could pick up from calm. Any E or NE direction should have shifted through NW
– low or trough stuck to the west maybe for days or possibly for hours. There will be shifts but they are usually minor	– stay more or less fixed to the present direction but there will always be shifts as weak troughs and ridges pass. Eventually there should be cyclonic shifts as low moves over	– same as now
– probably a fast-moving wave low will move through in a few hours' time. However, it could be more than six hours away	– return to direction it had before the wave began to influence the local wind. If not, is the wave developing into something bigger?	– more backed. Possible SE or S

continued

Table 13.1
continued

Gradient direction	High cloud	Barometer
NW to N following a depression just gone	From NW or N at easily noticeable speed	Rising but not for long
E	From S with noticeable speed	Falling or will soon begin to fall
E	From W or NW with noticeable speed	Slight fall or even a slight rise
E	From around E also	Indeterminate

low and its fronts and the relative position of the yacht. In Britain gale summaries come out at 0800 amd 1030, for example for North Atlantic from Northwood Fax. Thus you are well forewarned of likely trouble. The progress of the actual weather can be followed by sky observation, etc. as discussed earlier. Use the fax schedules to refine all your predictions.

FOLLOWING PROGRESS OF THE LOW
Use continuity ideas to find position of low and its central pressure. Basic charts here are last midnight or midday analysis (comes out three to four hours after H hour) and the H + 24 forecast (usually an hour or so later). Movement can be followed from the 1800 and 0600 analyses prior to H hour up to H hour and then your continuity ideas can be confirmed using your own drawing up of the actual plotted points for the following 0600 or 1800 respectively. (Preliminary points over limited region are broadcast within 1½ hours, but extensive coverage means waiting three or more hours.)

Compare latest actual and H + 24 charts of 500 mb contours (– or look at actual or forecast winds for flight level 180 (18 000 ft). Lows tend to steer by these winds, and so you can see where the low is most likely to go. FL 300 or thereabouts will enable you to see at a glance where the jet stream is. Any arrows with double triangles on them mean any low on the equatorial side is a candidate for deepening rapidly. Here we deal with travelling lows, and if the low in question seems to be close to closed contours on the 700 and 500 mb charts it is not travelling by our definition.

FOLLOWING PROGRESS OF THE FRONTS
Again your first stab at a frontal position for a not too distant future time will be continuity between H and H + 24 charts spanning this time. Remember that warm fronts move at two-thirds of the gradient behind them and cold fronts at gradient speed resolved perpendicularly across them. So use your geostrophic scales to move on a front from its most recent actually known position. This refines timing.

Also gain ideas of how the wind will shift as the front passes. Is the wind backing ahead of it? What degree of shift is to be expected at passage, and is it sharp or a more gradual shift with time? Look at wind directions at stations on recent actual charts which you know surround the front.

Fronts can also be located from the shape

Expect	Later wind should:	Wind was:
– wind will change anticyclonically through a short-lived weak ridge between the two lows	– pick up from a southerly point accompanied by advancing high cloud. So read 'S – moderate increasing', etc. depending on wind speed and direction	– cyclonic due to the passage of the low
– wind to become more cyclonic so possibly backing somewhat. Most likely to stay E and strengthen	– back N and decrease. Mainly fair becoming showery and colder. Sometimes if low is developing wind could increase from new direction	– almost any direction but speed would have been light to moderate
– coming low to track to south so probably no great wind increase. Could even lighten	– do as above but as low is probably well to the south could stay E. Should return to fair weather	– probably SE and has backed
– situation to be associated with a sluggish cyclonic situation covering whole area. So expect cyclonic shifts interspersed with anticyclonic shifts	– show no great change as long as lower and upper winds stay roughly in same direction. However, remarks as previous column apply here	– almost any direction including the present one of E

of the temps that have been made through them (see Part Two). You can see if subsidence is occurring and so weakening them from the way the humidity space goes pencil-like through the frontal cloud and then suddenly broadens into dryness above.

PREDICTING WIND

The surface wind at any future time must be predicted from the gradient. You know what the computer thinks the wind will be at H + 24 and you know what it actually is now. So use ideas as on page 73 to find direction changes for some hours ahead and advise tactician accordingly. Time of frontal passage is of vital importance here.

FORECASTING WEATHER

Charts do not contain weather, but some stations give a significant wind and weather prognosis early in the morning for the following day (Northwood 0340 for example). This will help clothe naked charts with weather. Otherwise your knowledge of met. will be given a full airing as you struggle to determine what weather will go with what features of the forecast charts. In the specific case covered here, read table 13.1 and dip into Part Two as required.

The sky signs and the points to look for if you have charts have been covered on previous pages. In table 13.1 we analyse the likely shift patterns depending on the wind and weather at the time of starting observations. Whatever the surface wind direction is, the crossed-winds rule for cyclonic development (page 148) must be being obeyed if the situation is to develop cyclonically.

Before any analysis can be done we have to get a reliable direction for the gradient wind (wind at about 2000 ft). This can come from direction of flight of low cloud, from weather charts or a call to a weather office, etc. Most times the surface wind is not widely different from the gradient wind, but it can be when (a) seabreezes or land breezes blow, or (b) when low inversions exist as happens during the evening, during the night and in the early morning, or (c) when surface winds are guided by high ground, etc.

As well as the signs of coming deterioration as outlined on page 152 we can gauge the track of an advancing depression from the gradient wind direction.

The table is written for the Northern Hemisphere. Readers in the Southern Hemisphere will have to change the directions to apply to their own lows and highs.

14 HEAVY WEATHER

What is heavy weather depends on the crew of an otherwise well-found craft. It is nearly always the crew who give up before the boat does and this was well illustrated in the notorious Fastnet Race of 1979 when half of the 15 fatalities were among those who abandoned their craft and took to the life rafts. All their craft were subsequently found afloat.

The family cruiser may well be in difficulties in Force-6 winds when these combine with an adverse seaway, and it was the wave conditions and not the wind which produced the incredible carnage in the 1979 Fastnet. In that race the winds blew at many different speeds from a mere 25 kn. to 55–60 kn. or more (hurricane force) and it was the variation in wind speed over relatively narrow bands of ocean that was the main cause of the knock-downs, roll-overs, pitch-poles, etc. that occurred.

The weather conditions that contribute to well-found yachts being put in danger include, of course, wind speed. But that is by no means all the story. The sea conditions that go with the wind field have an even greater part to play and it has been found that in the deep ocean wastes unusual and little understood sets of local conditions conspire to induce capsizing situations. These situations need not be recognised by, nor forecast by, the meteorological services. The deep-sea mariner either avoids the areas where such events may occur or he meets them and survives through a combination of good seamanship and luck.

The individual stories of the rogue winds and waves met by sailors crossing the oceans show that occasionally immense waves occur for which there seems to be no sufficient reason. The wind may be blowing no harder than before when one of these monsters rears above the hapless yacht. Yet the giant wave appears, does its worst and is gone. Because the stories are of individual events, no one can say how far from or near to the yacht similar conditions obtained. All we know is that a singular event occurred – the craft and crew survived – and we do not know about those who did not.

There are excellent books on sailing boats through heavy weather, among them the classic *Heavy Weather Sailing* by the late K. Adlard Coles (Ref. 7) and *Handling*

Small Boats in Heavy Weather by Frank Robb (Ref. 12). Any crew member who goes offshore should read these or any similar books he can find. If he meets the ultimate wave, then according to Robb nothing, be it large or small, can come through the experience unscathed. When such waves have been accurately measured at between 80 and 120 ft high, this is an obvious conclusion. They also look different from more normal waves, having an almost vertical leading face arched over a 'hole in the sea' which opens before them. Aircraft carriers and other big ships have their superstructures bent and twisted by such 'green ones', and yachts can only hope to survive the inevitable 360° roll or the, worse, 360° pitch-pole. Sea anchors, warps, etc. are simply swept towards the hapless yacht by the great speed of the top section of these immense waves. Thus while towing warps, lying ahull and riding to sea anchors all have their advocates in the more 'normal' conditions that go with gale-force winds (and undoubtedly they work), none of these can prevent the dismasting of a yacht under bare poles as the force of the water tosses her over. A scientifically measured event with an 80 ft wave at a weather ship off Ireland showed that it took just seven seconds for the wave to lift the ship and another seven to drop it into the succeeding trough.

The yacht would be in a better position than a bigger ship to ride such waves were it not that the rogue wave has a steeper than normal face up which the cockle-shell of the yacht cannot possibly be lifted. It has to go under at some point on the all but vertical face of the wave. Undoubtedly when the monster wave appears (and they can be seen sometimes on radar), extreme speed is required to secure whatever can be secured and to get below and batten down. There appears to be no other course of action as more becomes known of the attributes and shape of such waves.

Research shows that the velocity of the peak of ordinary waves is something of the order of a third of the phase velocity, i.e. the speed of the wave as a whole. The internal circulation well known as explaining the dynamics of relatively small waves is normal. When you get a breaking wave the difference is that the peak velocity exceeds the phase velocity, the wave front steepens and the top curls over to fall down the face. The monster wave is a breaking wave in deep water. In this it parallels the breakers over the shallows (see fig. 14.1).

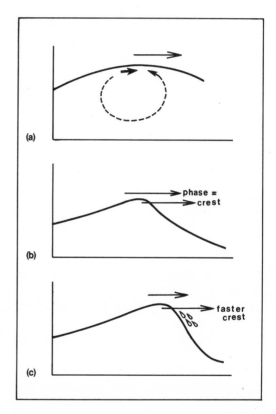

Fig. 14.1 *Deep-water breaking waves. (a) is a normal wave where the velocity of the wave as a whole (phase velocity) is much greater than the velocity of the crest. There is a relative rotation of the water in the wave. (b) is a wave on the point of becoming* a breaking wave where the phase velocity and the crest velocity are about the same value. (c) is the breaking wave where the crest velocity exceeds the phase velocity, and the inevitable result is that the top of the wave falls down the face.

After the Fastnet disaster Olin Stephens, Karl Kirkman and Robert Peterson (Ref. 14) brought together the available research on the kind of wave conditions that obtained during that notorious race. Their paper 'Sailing yacht capsizing' produced some important clues about what may be the answer to the rogue wave conditions. In the Fastnet there was, for the first time, the chance to sample the pressure, wind and whole wave field along a rhumb line that stretched from the Scillies to the Fastnet Rock. The yachts were contained within a narrow swathe as the wind was more or less SW and so the legs were both free in either direction. In the past the lone yacht has met one of what could be many such waves, but has had no means of knowing this. In the Fastnet a whole gaggle of well-found and well-crewed craft – the best in the world – experienced ultimate waves in many different places. It is worth considering what has been learned for the benefit of others who may have to meet similar conditions.

A vast library of information exists about the effects of this race on craft and crew, but the meteorological conditions needed deeper research than was possible via the medium of the weather questions framed in the official Fastnet Race Enquiry. At this time the late K. Adlard Coles was preparing a new edition of his book *Heavy Weather Sailing* and prepared his own questionnaire. The detailed replies to Adlard Coles'' enquiry included complete barometric records from many of the largest yachts, and thus it was possible for the very first time to plot an hour-by-hour graph of the pressure readings experienced by a fleet of yachts in extremis conditions (Ref. 18).

By using the barometric readings from St Mary's, Scilly, as an accurate yardstick it was possible to check the barometers of the yachts as they passed Scilly. They were remarkably accurate, only differing by a millibar or two from the St Mary's read-

ings. When the results were plotted I was astonished to find that there were 'holes' in what should have been a fairly consistent fall of pressure along the rhumb line Scilly to Fastnet Rock. The low centre was accurately tracked a hundred miles north as it moved in from the Atlantic over the Shannon Estuary, but there were what seemed to be subsidiary lows quasi-stationary over the rhumb line. As these could not be lows in the accepted sense I have christened them 'cyclonic pools', but their exact nature and the reasons for them being there are still a mystery to me. It is as if great whirlpools spun off the end of south-west Ireland and slowly moved down over the Fastnet fleet. However, such an idea would be wrong in that while the pressure fell there was no sign of the tornado-like properties that the word 'whirlpool' engenders.

Where the 'pools' were at 2100Z and 0000Z (2200 and 0100 BST) is revealed by the barometer readings of the leading yachts (fig. 14.2a). The first casualties of the night coincided with being in the vicinity of the Labadie Bank where the first and deepest pool, A, formed. That this pool was there at 1800Z is confirmed from fig. 14.2b, but the leaders were beyond this developing pool and so only really encountered problems after they rounded the Rock and headed back into this 'sea of trouble'.

The great variation in the conditions experienced by yachts within short distances of one another can be explained on two counts. The plots of reported wind strength show that storm-force winds developed on either side of the pools leading to very high waves being bred in corridors with lesser wind and waves between. Secondly it depended on where a yacht was as to whether it encountered very bad conditions or not.

In *Fastnet Force 10* John Rousmaniere (Ref. 13) has this to say: 'the danger of the waves lay not in their height but in their shape'. George Tinley, who had been so

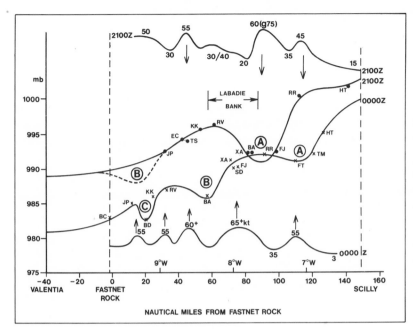

Fig. 14.2a   *The First Watch of the Fastnet night. The barometer readings of the yachts at 2100Z (GMT) and 0000Z reveal how the Pools A and B moved during this time and how a third Pool, C, had entered the area by midnight. The curves above and below indicate the speed of the wind as recorded at these times by the yachts, and they indicate how the 'wind corridors' developed either side of the pools in almost all cases. In order not to make the diagram confusing the situation at 1800Z has been combined with that for 0300Z.*

Key to the observers:
BA *Black Arrow,*
BC *Battlecry,*
BD *Blaue Dolphyn,*
BV *Bonaventure,*
EC *Eclipse,* FJ *Firanjo,*

FN *Finnibar,* FT *Fluter,*
HT *Hurricantoo,*
JP *Jan Pott,* KK *Kukri,*
PN *Pordin Nancy,*
RR *Right Royal,*

RV *Revolootion,*
SD *Sandettie,*
TM *Trumpeter,*
TR *Tiderace,*
TS *Toscana,* XA *Xara.*

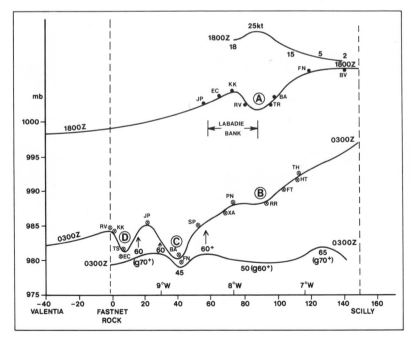

Fig. 14.2b   *As early as 7 p.m. (BST = GMT + 1 h) winds were rising in association with the development of Pool A. By the end of the night A had disappeared, B was all but rubbed out, but C and a new one D had entered the scene. However, by now the entire wind field was at least 45–50 kn. Thus the variations in the wind-speed curve are shallower than they appear in fig. 14.2a. Key as in fig. 14.2a.*

badly beaten around in his *Windswept*, later
said, 'There were seas coming at one angle
with breakers on them, but there were seas
coming at another angle also with breakers,
and then there were the most fearsome
things where the two met in the middle.'
Chris Bouzaid, an experienced ocean-racing
sailor who was the helmsman of *Police Car*
(an Australian 42 ft boat) described the
conditions in *Yachting* magazine. 'Every sea
was different. Some of them we would
square away and run down the front of,
others were just too steep to do this. One
imagines a sea to be a long sausagelike piece
of water moving across the ocean. However, this was not the case at all as these seas
had too many breaks in them and were not
uniform.'

These descriptions square with the idea
that corridors of extremely strong winds
generated immense waves, and that these
spread sideways across the lesser wave fields
between, but that as the distance between
one storm corridor and the next was not
great, so the spreading waves could at times
meet and produce the effect described by
Tinley. The kind of thing that was occurring is shown in fig. 14.3, and X marks the
centre of a 40-mile-diameter circle in which
most of the casualties occurred. It is seen to
be in the centre between the storm corridors
that developed either side of Pool A
between midnight and 0300Z. Similar conditions would have occurred in two or three
other places in association with the other
pools.

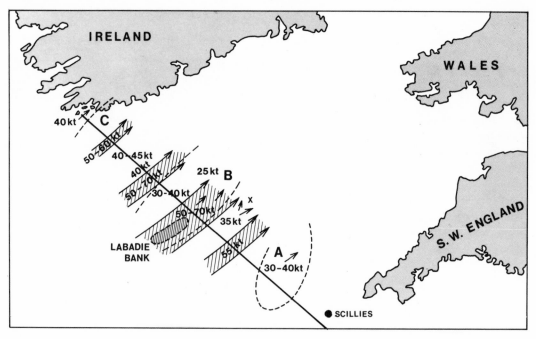

Fig. 14.3   *When the winds reported between midnight and 0300Z are plotted they reveal wind corridors with violent-storm or hurricane-force winds interspersed by zones of normal gale force. A few yachts reported only Force 6–7. It is these 'storm corridors' that created the impossible seaway. A, B and C refer to the positions of the cyclonic pools revealed in fig. 14.2a.*

That such waves are very like those generated by hurricanes is shown in fig. 14.4. Admittedly the 42 ft wave recorded at another time off the Irish coast is nothing compared with the 75 ft one recorded in Hurricane Camille, but the same shape of wave-train occurs in both and the important connection is that in hurricanes the change in wind speed outwards from the eye is very great. It was similar horizontal changes of wind speed that were evident on the night of the Fastnet disaster. The authors of Ref. 14 on which fig. 14.4 is based have shown that unlike lesser waves the frictional drag of hurricane-force winds on the sea builds giant waves almost instantaneously. Thus locally stronger winds can build the extreme waves in a very short time. This is an important observation when thinking of the reasons for rogue seas.

These observations provide some clues to the problem of survival storms. Stories of strange and immense waves encountered at sea abound and very few reasons can be given for them. The production of local storm-force wind corridors in an otherwise gale-force wind field could supply the reason for some of these encounters with rogue waves which may be more prevalent than is often thought. It is only very occasionally that a storm of the dimensions of the Fastnet storm springs up in summer, and even when it does it may be that no yacht is within the compass of its worst conditions. Luckily, therefore, the Fastnet disaster of 13/14 August 1979 is something that is only likely to occur once in twenty years and in fact is unprecedented in the annals of ocean racing. Otherwise the worst storms in the North Atlantic and North Pacific occur in the depths of winter when no yachts are at sea, but it would seem that the worst seas occur in association with the troughs that follow the passage of cold fronts of very deep lows (Ref. 8). This puts cold air under warm which is unstable and so allows for strong updraughts. It is

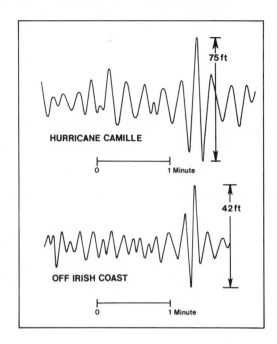

Fig. 14.4   *Wave recorders can show the immense size of some localised (episodic) waves. Because those in a hurricane resemble one taken off the Irish coast, it is evident that similar conditions of horizontal wind shear exist in both instances, only the amplitude of the waves being different.*

possible that updraughts over Fastnet allowed the local wind increases to occur (Ref. 17) there and so produced the survival conditions.

Another important way of generating giant waves is any form of 'wind-against-tide' phenomenon at sea. Winds directed against the full flood of the Gulf Stream off America or the Agulhas Current off the south-east coast of South Africa cause giant breaking waves. In a 4 kn. opposing current the winds build short-period waves that steepen to a point where they curl over and break, and in these conditions waves of all periods are increased in amplitude.

The location and temperature of the Gulf Stream are broadcast regularly by Norfolk Fax both on a large Western Atlantic and a small East Coast of the US scale. Thus in

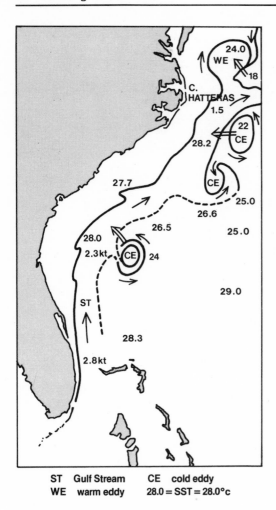

ST   Gulf Stream   CE   cold eddy
WE   warm eddy   28.0 = SST = 28.0°c

Fig. 14.5 *A means of avoiding possible trouble areas. A Gulf Stream analysis for 0300Z 9 July 1982 showing where cold and warm eddies exist as well as the speed of the current. The double arrows show where there are thermal gradients sufficient to produce wind if the air is unstable in their vicinity. CE = Cold eddy; ST = Gulf Stream; WE = warm eddy; SST = sea surface temperature; 28.0 = SST = 28°C.*

fig. 14.5 (which is for 0300Z 9 July 1982), should an intense depression develop north of the Bahamas, the conditions for giant waves off Florida are there as the opposing current is nearly 3 kn. Water temperatures are given which allow one to see where the strong thermal gradients are in your area. Winds will tend to blow out of the colder parts into the warm eddies, and this, added to a generally gale-force pressure pattern orientated for winds in the same direction, can add an extra impetus to create the waves already described.

In quiet conditions the thermal gradients found here and elsewhere, which can now be measured by satellite observation, will often explain an odd cant to the wind as minor forms of 'seabreezes' develop into the surrounding sea area. These sharp temperature differences may also lead to local areas of more than usually strong convection currents which can induce sudden and peculiar gust conditions or may add to existing wind to produce locally strong winds when the gradient indicates no such thing. Anywhere where cold upwellings occur into a warmer body of water is also a place where the deep-sea mariner should look out for oddities of wind behaviour.

Such considerations may account in part for such tragedies as the loss of the three-masted sailing ship *Marques* which foundered with the eighteen people below given no time to escape. The barque was overwhelmed by a monstrous wave during the Bermuda–Halifax leg of the Tall Ships Race at about 0800Z Sunday 3 June 1984. According to survivors hurricane-force winds hit the ship 'out of the blue' and rolled her on to her side. Yet the chart for 0600Z that day showed gradient winds over the area no higher than 25 kn. Admittedly there was a trough crossing the area from a complex low to the north of the area, but nothing to indicate that winds of sufficient strength could be generated. Such mysteries add to the sum total of events that make people sincerely believe that there are unexplained forces at work in the so-called Bermuda Triangle, as the catalogue of odd disappearances in the area is very long. It shows that we are still ignorant of local forces that can create survival conditions for some and nothing like the same ferocity for others who are nearby.

15 ABOUT SHOWERY AIRSTREAMS

On the whole showers come with cool airstreams because the situation of cold air over a warmer surface is an unstable one. Instability sends bubbles (thermals) of warm air up to a height which is limited by the air cooling to a temperature that is the same as itself. Thus the cloud tops are where the air has found an isothermal layer or an inversion of some kind and cannot rise any further. (Look at tops in photo R7.)

It has been found that heavy rain of any kind cannot occur unless the temperature has fallen to below −13°C and so heavy showers demand deep clouds. Such clouds are called cumulonimbus (Cb) meaning heap clouds bearing rain, and for the layman the difference between a big cumulus cloud and a small cumulonimbus cloud is that the latter rains and the former does not. Over the sea the most likely time for heavy showers is during the early hours of the morning, whereas over land it is during the afternoon. In coastal districts there is often a double shower maximum with onshore winds – the sea one around dawn and the land one in the afternoon.

Showers are important to yachtsmen because of the gusts and squalls they bring (photo C.21). They may temporarily cut visibility substantially and when they are of snow they will cut it to fog limits or lower. They also bring a micro-wind-shift pattern that backs the wind ahead and veers it behind the big showers (NH).

Showers tend to come also in crops more or less stretched across the wind in trough lines (photo C.18). These trough lines are preceded and followed by clearer periods in many instances. This is because the ascending air in the trough sinks both ahead and behind to produce inversions that limit the height to which the clouds can grow (fig. 15.1).

For want of time and to avoid too much complexity the term 'showers' will appear in forecasts when the rain from layer clouds is intermittent. Such rain may be thundery in nature, i.e. big spots which start suddenly and just as suddenly stop. Thundery showers will usually be mentioned as such in the forecasts, but here some thunder and lightning is also to be expected (photo C.24).

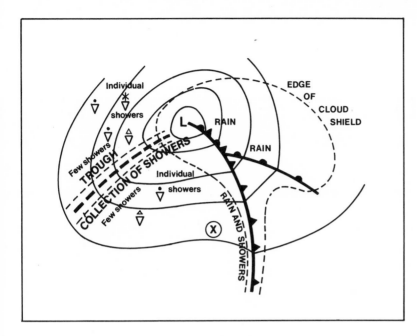

Fig. 15.1 *Where to expect showers in the circulation of a normal depression. If there are fewer showers than there ought to be, is there an airmass trough upwind?*

Clear skies over land in the morning may grow to big cumulus during the forenoon and into showers by lunch-time or the afternoon (photo C.17). Sometimes they develop enough to become thunderstorms, and the high time for these is the afternoon into the evening (photo C.20). Further, clear airstreams with on-shore wind directions will often develop cloud and showers over the slopes and tops of higher ground inland. Equally, with wind that is directed off-shore over high land, the growth of showers over the hills or mountains will leave less moisture for the showers in their lee and they will die out over the coast and the sea. Suggestions as to how to assess the showery situation are now given.

SHOWERS

General situation

The showers considered are those that occur in relatively cool maritime polar airstreams typically in the rear of departing depressions.

Without fax

FORECAST SOURCES
(a) Domestic radio for land areas (advise about showers, maximum air temperature distribution in time, whether heavy and gusty).
(b) Domestic radio shipping forecasts (advise about oceanic showers, some indication of time; give actual reports from coastal stations).
(c) Same forecasts on Navfax.
(d) TV (time-lapse presentations of showery airstreams, general shape of the weather chart and some forecast charts, day and night maximum and minimum temperatures, vague indications of surface wind, occasional mention of gusts. Polar orbital or geostationary satellite pictures showing extent of shower fields).
(e) VHF from coast radio stations.
(f) Marine telephone forecasts for coasts and coastal waters.
(g) Your own present weather together with inferences from state of sky, air and sea temperatures, etc.

GENERAL CONSIDERATIONS
Oceanic airstreams:

(a)   showers occur by day and night (more likely overnight).
(b)   trough lines occur day or night; grouped showers (and maybe more continuous rain) preceded and followed by clearer (often shower-free) periods.
(c)   frontal troughs produce showers like (b) but (unlike (b)) airmass changes. Establishment of coldest airmass may be across two or three consecutive cold fronts.

Overland airstreams:

(a)   showers by day but not by night (diurnal variations).
(b)   airmass troughs develop away from windward coasts by day with clearer (often shower-free) periods before and after. (Not the same as (b) above, which are recurrent features of the circulation of depressions.)
(c)   showers may be only orographic and so areas downwind of hill and mountain ridges are relatively free of showers.

YOUR SITUATION
In an oceanic airstream, if showers are going to occur they will already be occurring because sea temperature (S) and air temperature (T) will not change until airmass changes. (See Airmasses in Part Two.) So look around for signs of the fuzzy-grey stalks between cloud and sea that indicate heavy showers falling (photo C.21). However, remember that cold upwellings, or crossing currents like the Gulf Stream, can suddenly alter S.

In an overland airstream, check your S against forecast minimum T overnight to see if night showers can occur (that does not mean to say they will). Check forecast maximum T by day against actual air temperature (B) at breakfast-time. If T exceeds B by 5 to 10°C, expect showers by early afternoon, if not before.

If forecast showers do not occur, in an oceanic airstream subsidence from high up is the most likely reason. That should make you think of the next trough upwind or the next depression forming. Have there been signs of a change of airmass that the forecasters may have missed? In this case T must have risen – unless S has fallen because you have entered a colder bit of water. (Also read remarks below.) In an overland airstream, again subsidence that depresses the cloud tops is the first thing to look for. Do not expect showers until land heats up. Have the showers all rained themselves away on hills or mountains upwind? Has an upper cloud veil or layer cut off the sun and so stopped convection?

Remember that troughs gather all the showers to themselves and so a shower-free period may simply herald some concentrated showers and/or rain to come soon. A cloud-mass with elevated tops (and maybe an anvil or two) on the windward horizon will most likely be an airmass trough (photo C.18.)

REASONS FOR SEEKING INFORMATION
On the macroscale, showery airstream precludes fog: on the contrary, visibility is usually good to excellent. On the mesoscale, wind backs ahead of showery trough lines and veers behind. On the microscale, wind veers and increases sharply as a shower starts (gusty squalls). It backs and decreases as the shower passes.

With fax

YACHT'S POSITION SIMILAR TO X IN FIG. 15.1
Cold front just passed – visibility excellent – big Cu clouds about, but not necessarily any showers at the moment; wind typically WSW–NW, Force 5–6. Are showers going to occur, and what is the longer-term situation? (Photo C.15.)

C.1 *(above) Jet cirrus taken at roughly the same time as C.3 and C.4. Note the cirrus fallstreaks congregating into bands which is so typical of jet cirrus as opposed to the cirrus of lesser systems as in photo 5.1.*

C.2 *(below) A characteristic of the most virile form of jet cirrus is the way there is a sharp cut-off between cloud (equatorial side) and blue sky (polar side) of either hemisphere. This sky nearly always means trouble.*

C.3 *This picture should be read in conjunction with C.4 as they were taken within a few minutes of one another. Note the way the aircraft trail has moved compared with the horizon in this short time. That means the cirrus bands are definitely moving at high jet speeds.*

C.4 *This picture together with photos C.1 and
C.3 were of the jet that broke one of the longest blocks in the
westerlies of recent times over Atlantic Europe (September
1976).*

C.5 (above) When assessing upper winds you can use trails. If they shred sideways and widen rapidly, the wind is across them. If they raise little battlements along their backs, the wind is along them, as here.

C.6 (below) Upper wind (cirrus), lower wind (gradient shown by cumulus) and surface wind (wind vane) in one picture. They are all going to be in different directions except under rare circumstances.

C.7   (above) Coming warm front or occlusion.
Stratocumulus dies out below while As invades the higher
sky. This kind of rapid build-up cannot amount to much.

C.8   (right) When cirrus clouds lose their hooked
appearance and fall straight down the sky (as here) or when
their filaments, sheaves, etc. lie in crossed directions all
around the sky, it signifies no definite change of wind with
height and so light upper winds. That indicates no
development in the weather.

C.9   (left) Evening is a time for seeing which cloud layer
lies above which and what they mean for the night. Lower
clouds get shadowed first and give evening clouds their
characteristic contrast.

C.10   (below) Is this jet cirrus? It may have been once, or
it could be aircraft trails. It was easy to tell that this only
meant 'no change' as the lower wind and the clouds both
moved from north-east (13 June 1968 in East Anglia).

C.11 *(above) The characteristic 'sun in his house' halo about the sun indicates cirrostratus and so the high risk that the following clouds will be those of bad weather.*

C.12 *(below) When the halo has gone and the sun disappears wanly into the gathering altostratus, you can be pretty sure that rain will follow. Wind may have already begun to increase. If not look out for strong wind later.*

OCEANIC AND OVERLAND AIRSTREAMS

Obtain 'plotted points' chart nearest to present time and look for ∇ symbols at positions upwind (also include ($\bigtriangledown$), or ($\bullet$)). If in doubt use 700 mb contours to determine what is 'upwind'. Remember a day's heating sets off showers over land but not over sea. Look for cyclonic isobars upwind on the latest actual surface chart and compare with previous charts to see how the trough line may be moving. Check station reports to see what the distribution of showers is. Any sign of thunderstorms?

FORECAST YOUR OWN SHOWER RISK

Do this by obtaining a temp upwind in the airstream. Use your S and a reliable dewpoint temperature from a station closely upwind with an exposure as close to your own as possible. So find cloudbase and cloud tops on the temp (see page 194). If tops go higher than −13°C isotherm, then heavy showers are pretty certain.

From sea isotherm chart. This could be yesterday's or even the day before's, but check with your own sea temperature: get your S and a reliable air temperature T from a station upwind. If S greater than T, then showers are possible and Cu clouds pretty certain. If T greater than S, then showers cannot occur: expect much layer cloud at various levels and there is risk of fog (not a problem here; see page 160). Look further upwind along the isobars to the origin of the airstream coming your way. Use T from same stations over a few recent charts to see if T is falling with time, i.e. the airstream is getting colder out of its source region. If so shower risk will increase.

Check the nephanalysis for an estimate of what shower fields exist to windward and so whether you are in their path.

Finally check the progress of your forecast from sky signs and wind direction changes. Do they accord with the expectations? If not, some of the reasons are to be found earlier in this section. Look at the H + 24 forecast surface chart to see what may be the trouble.

Further ahead. Having forecast a showery airstream, check isobar spacing and orientation for the area in question over several forecast charts, i.e. H + 48, H + 36 and H + 24 as the time approaches. Confirm or otherwise with the latest 'plotted points' chart on which you have drawn reliable isobars and used your geostrophic scale to obtain the gradient wind speed.

GUST SPEED

Some fax stations give 850 mb or 1000 mb wind speed and direction. This will give a good estimate of the maximum gust speed out of showers. Expect more at the head of heavy showers. If you measure gradient from latest actual chart, then this 2000 ft wind will probably underestimate the maximum gusts. The gradient direction will also be the gust direction.

GENERAL TACTICAL CONSIDERATIONS

With individual shower clouds expect the wind to double in speed between, out of and in showers and to shift clockwise (veer) as squall strikes. Note that major thunderstorms do the opposite, i.e. back. Thus the sails carried must be assessed on the possibility of such gusts. The helmsman can gain advantage if he expects to get a lift on starboard as the gusts strike and a lift on port as the shower passes. Trough lines normally bring a progressive backing of possibly 30° or more as they approach. The squall line may back even further, followed by an hour or so of showers and/or rain during which wind generally veers to a direction more veered than before the trough struck. If beating, taking port tack to enter the trough will produce a lift, but care must be taken to meet wind-shifts in gusts.

16 SEA TEMPERATURES

Once upon a time the temperature of the deep ocean, or anywhere where ships did not ply as a matter of course, was often an unknown quantity. This is no longer the case. Satellites using their radiometers can sample the sea surface temperature in a routine manner and so continuous monitoring of the ocean surface occurs. This information is available to the yachtsman either on an enquiry basis or via facsimile, and fig. 16.1 shows the kind of sea temperature plot for the North Atlantic that is broadcast as routine from stations such as Norfolk VA and Quickborn. The National Oceanographic Centre also broadcasts similar information for shipping in the North Atlantic via the Northwood fax transmitter. Similar information on all the oceans will be available from the centres that cover those areas. The change in sea temperature over a period of several days is also included and so it is easy to find out if the sea in any area of interest is changing significantly either up or down (not shown in fig. 16.1).

Sea temperature has a profound effect on a person's survival when he or she is lost overboard, and there are definite criteria as to how long one can last. In *Heavy Weather Sailing* (Ref. 7), K. Adlard Coles gives, in an Appendix concerning the air/sea rescue during the 1979 Fastnet Race, a graph that shows the limits of safety. This diagram is reproduced here (fig. 16.2), and the remarks made should be studied by those who go to sea when temperatures are anywhere near the marginal or fatal ones.

Spring is the most dangerous time for yachting because spring weather invites people out before the sea temperature has had a chance to respond to increasing solar radiation. The example of 8 April 1986 (fig. 16.1) includes figures in circles that are the safe survival times. For example, off Spain, because the sea temperature is 15°C (59°F) and in a reasonable seaway, there is a two-hour chance of survival without incurring the onset of hypothermia. However, off Cape Cod, anyone lost in the 5°C water temperature there would have a mere half-hour's chance of survival. Similarly in the cold waters of the North Sea there would be the same short period when the body might withstand hypothermia providing

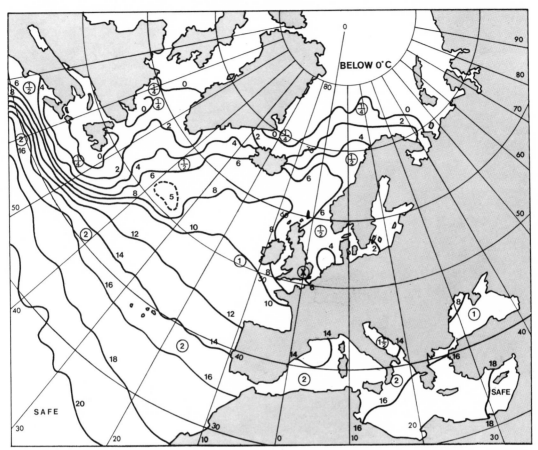

Fig. 16.1 (above) North
Atlantic sea temperatures
in degrees Celsius for 8
April 1986. These charts
will also show the change
over a period of several
days prior to the
verification date. For
example the cold pool in
mid-Atlantic has fallen
by over 4°C in the past 5
days: does that mean
icebergs? The remarkable
change in water
temperature off
Newfoundland is due to
the Gulf Stream meeting
the Labrador Current:
fog, showers, strange
thermally induced winds?
The figures in circles are
the safe survival times
in hours in the water
temperatures obtaining
at this time.

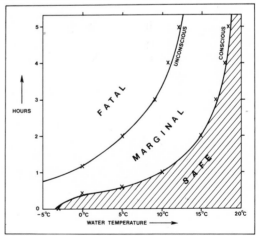

Fig. 16.2   The chances
of survival if lost
overboard in the normal
range of sea
temperatures. An hour at
50°F (10°C) will have

the lost person on the
edge of marginal
hypothermia. Constant
battering of waves has
also to be taken into
account.

little movement was involved and the wind was light enough not to continually batter the lost person with waves.

Another aspect of the sea temperature plots is to show where there are steep temperature gradients. These are regions where, should the wind blow from cold water to warmer water, sudden and intense convection currents could occur so leading to squalls and, if not squalls, at least to sudden and possibly local increases in wind strength over and above what might be expected from the forecast. We see such a zone south of Newfoundland where the Gulf Stream slides along the cold waters of the Labrador Current. The sea temperature gradient here is extremely steep, and such a region might best be avoided if possible. The figures in circles show that on the southerly side of the gradient there is a two-hour survival chance, while not far away on the northern side there is a mere quarter of an hour. Where the chart is marked 'Safe' we are above the 20°C (68°F) isotherm and sea temperature is no longer a factor in survival.

If the wind should blow the opposite way, i.e. from the warm water to the cold, then fog is very likely. The warm air will be able to hold much water vapour and will be tending to stability so that its tendency is to sink towards the sea surface. The area around Newfoundland is notorious for the extensive fog banks that form due to the clash of the warm Gulf Stream and the cold Labrador Current.

Over northern seas the last isotherm drawn is for 0°C (32°F). Sea water, being impure due to salt and other dissolved substances, will remain liquid below the normal freezing point of pure water. Thus this region is just marked 'Below 0°C'.

Drawing on personal experience of the period of fig. 16.1 on the Essex coast (X), it was a time of very unstable air over this region of East Anglia and because of the very low North Sea temperatures and the strength of the early April sun the morning

periods were mainly sunny. Then, when the sun had saturated the ground with heat, the showers grew. They grew big and provided extensive periods of rain, sleet and snow – this was one of the coldest springs for many years. However, the major inference for early sailors was that this was also a recipe for seabreezes because the sun only had to warm the land surfaces a little and the breeze was in. In effect what happened almost every day was that the wind from around north clashed with the cool, moist air from the sea and a zone of more than usually intense showers formed more or less parallel to the coast. On Wednesday 2 April the seabreeze frontal trough got about 10 miles inland. There it stopped and cascaded wintry precipitation on to us who were under it for most of the afternoon. On the next day the same thing happened except the trough made another five miles or so. The coastal areas were mainly fair while all this was going on inland. I know this because on the Friday I went out to the Suffolk coast and found continuous sunshine while those inland were deluged by showers.

Thus sea temperature information can be of great use when assessing the likelihood of seabreezes setting in. The seabreeze will assert itself very readily, and in circumstances when you otherwise might not expect it, when it is spring and the sea has not yet warmed up. In years like 1986, in British home waters the breeze even blew when the sun did not really come out at all in any consistent way. The radiation through thin cloud layers was enough to induce the breeze to blow. Later in the year things would be different.

Looking at fig. 16.1 we would expect similar remarks to apply to the American coasts where the sea temperatures are even lower than in the North Sea. Strong seabreezes blow in the Baltic because of the low water temperatures whenever the spring or summer sun is out on the shores and the mountains. In general there will always be the potential to generate sea-breezes during the day over any coast except for those where more than averagely warm waters lie off the coast. For this reason autumn proves to be a poor time for seabreezes as the land cools and the sea retains its summer warmth.

17 WAVE HEIGHT

The height of waves depends on: wind speed; fetch – distance to nearest landmass; and duration for which the wind has blown in this direction. It will also depend on local conditions already mentioned, such as adverse current and any horizontal wind shear there may be across the direction of the wind.

The description of state of sea is given in table 17.1. Only seas that are slight or above have to be considered, and we can therefore provide a table for coastal waters (table 17.2). The heights in table 17.2 are those of the highest waves that are met with on a regular basis. However, waves higher than this will be met with, and on a statistical basis the chance of a yacht encountering one or more of these waves will increase with the duration of the storm.

Table 17.1 Description of sea state

Code figure	Descriptive term	Wave height	
		imperial	metric
0	calm (glassy)	0	0
1	calm (rippled)	0–4 in	0–0.1
2	smooth (wavelets)	4–20 in	0.1 –0.5
3	slight (S)	20 in–4 ft	0.5 –1.25
4	moderate (M)	4–8	1.25–2.5
5	rough (R)	8–13	2.5 –4
6	very rough (VR)	13–20	4–6
7	high (H)	20–30	6–9
8	very high (VH)	30–45	9–14
9	phenomenal (PH)	Over 45	Over 14

Table 17.2   Wave heights given fetch and duration

Fetch (Nm)	Description	Highest wave in storm[c]	Time to reach this height (hours)[a]
Force 4 (11–16 kn.) Moderate breeze			
10	S		2½
20	S		4
30	S		5
40	S		7
50	S		7
60	S		8
80	S		11
100	S		11
Force 5 (17–21 kn.) Fresh breeze			
10	S		2
20	S		3
30	M		4
40	M		6
50	M		6
60	M		7
80	M		10
100	M		11
200	M/R		20
Force 6 (22–27 kn.) Strong breeze			
10	S		2
20	M		3
30	M/R		4
40	R		5
50	R		5
60	R		6
80	R		9
100	R		10
200	R/VR		18[b]
Force 7 (28–33 kn.) Near gale			
10	M	7	1½
20	M/R	12	2
30	R	15	3
40	R	18	4
50	VR	21	5
60	VR	24	5
80	VR	24	9
100	VR	27	9
200	VR/H	32	18
Force 8 (34–40 kn.) Gale			
10	M	8	1½
20	R	17	2
30	VR	20	3
40	VR	25	4
50	VR	28	4
60	H	30	5
80	H	34	8
100	H	36	8
200	H	40	14
Force 9 (41–47 kn.) Severe gale[d]			
10	R	12	1½
20	VR	22	2
30	VR/H	28	2½
40	H	32	3
50	H	36	4
60	VH	40	5
80	VH	44	5½
100	VH	46	6½
200	VH	53	12
Force 10 (48–55 kn.) Storm			
10	R	14	1
20	VR/H	28	2
30	H	33	2
40	H/VH	40	3
50	VH	45	3½
60	VH	48	4
80	VH	53	5
100	VH	58	6
200	PH	65	12

[a] If the wind has not blown this long or has changed direction appreciably, lower the wave height accordingly.

[b] For the wind speeds, no highest wave is applicable.

[c] Increase the highest waves by 1½–2% for oceanic waves. Apart from fetches of 100–200 miles which overestimate the heights, the values given under 'Highest wave in storm' are also the regular maximum heights in the deep ocean)

[d] Apart from longer fetches the heights here are also the normal heights of oceanic waves.

WAVE-HEIGHT ANALYSIS AND PROGNOSIS

The wave field is predictable using the known relationships between wind strength, direction, fetch and duration, and the met. computers handle this aspect of 'weather' just as they do the weather charts. As the computer-generated prognoses of surface-pressure patterns are done on a routine basis and are found to be reliable in their large-scale predictions, it is a simple matter for computer-generated maps of significant wave height to be produced and broadcast. Such wave-height predictions can go out to as far ahead as the surface pressure pattern forecasts go, and 48-hour or longer wave prognoses are a regular feature of radio-fax broadcasts. Obviously

the weather centres, who also obtain these charts on a routine basis, will be able to answer the queries of yachtsmen as to the expected wave heights in any particular area. However, if the predictions are required in more detail than can be given over the phone, then the yachtsman has to seek out someone who has a fax and can take the charts for him to study. Merchantmen will have such fax equipment, as many will use it for weather routing exercises so that they can avoid the worst of the wind and the waves.

The kind of wave-height prognosis chart that might be obtained is shown in fig. 17.1. Here the figures are significant wave height in metres and this is based on the 12-hours-ahead forecast for midday on the Tuesday of the Fastnet Race disaster.

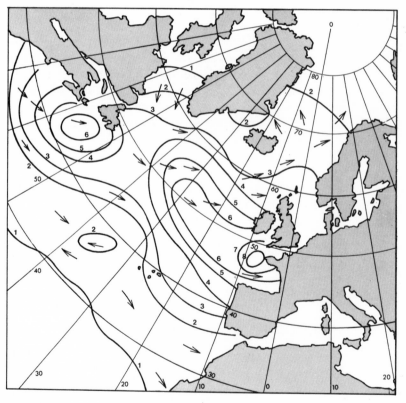

Fig. 17.1   *A 24-hour significant wave-height prediction for midnight of Monday 13 August 1979. The centre of the highest part of the wave field would be off Ushant according to the computer where the waves would be approaching 30 ft. The computer cannot yet allow for the rogue conditions that obtained south of Ireland that night.*

This chart was worked out by computer using actual data for midnight Monday (0000 Tuesday). It will be seen that by that time the average height of a third of the highest waves over the whole ocean surface (significant wave height definition) was expected to be 7 m or 23 ft. The highest waves of all were expected to be in a limited region off Ushant.

The arrows indicate the direction of the sea/swell in the example of fig. 17.1, but in other wave prognoses the sea is indicated by solid arrows and swell by broken ones. Centres of maximum and minimum wave height are also indicated on these forecast charts that are broadcast once a day from Bracknell and from other fax stations such as Norfolk who have taken the Bracknell chart by satellite.

The significant wave height information has to be considered in association with the relevant surface weather charts because, although the wave prognoses will indicate the centres of maximum seaway, they will not be able to give any information as to the incidence of rogue seas of the kind described for the 1979 Fastnet Race in chapter 14. It may be impossible for the ordinary yachtsman, whether he has a fax machine or not, to assess the likelihood of rogue waves, but unless forced to do so the best answer is to avoid the areas where trouble seems likely. Although a two-days-ahead wave forecast cannot be actually had until some hours after the observations were taken, it can still provide sufficient warning either to put off the trip or, if already at sea, to sail to avoid the expected centre of maximum seaway. The latter course is a part of weather-routing – a technique that has been in use by merchantmen with sensitive cargoes and tight time schedules for many years. The yacht cannot plan in the way that ships can. The wind goes light before many a storm and so very little way can be made. The pilot of a merchantman can say what his ship will do in the way of knots and so can confidently expect to be in a given position at a given time. Further, considering the scale of storm areas, the slow speed of the average yacht may make it impossible to be outside the danger zone in the time available. However, the acquisition of regular fax charts is a necessary prerequisite for any deep ocean-going yacht that intends to sail, say, the Atlantic by the direct route, or across any other expanse of green water when the voyage is expected to take weeks rather than days.

18   LIGHT WINDS

If you look up the Pilot for some of the areas covered in this book and consult the climatic information, it will usually include mean wind speeds for two times of day for twelve months of the year. The times will usually be early forenoon and early afternoon, because of the diurnal wind-speed variation which will be near its lowest at the early time and its maximum at the later time.

For example Malta lies in the Sicilian Channel between Italy and Africa and so is oceanic (even if the Mediterranean is not considered to be an ocean). When you consult the statistics you are struck by the very small difference between the afternoon and morning average wind speeds. Even in January there is only a 3-kn. difference between the 11 kn. at 0800 and the 14 kn. at 1400. Or at Skagen at the northernmost tip of Denmark, there is no difference whatsoever in the mean wind speed between 0800 and 1400 in any month other than November and December. The winter means tend to 13 kn. and the summer ones are all 9 kn.

As the bracket of light winds is, for us,

up to the limit of Force 3, i.e. 10 kn., so the average wind speeds in most places will not be much more than this even in the afternoon when they should be at their strongest. This tells us two things. First, there are more light winds than heavy ones and the statistics cloak the true state of affairs. It takes a lot of gales to force the mean speed up by a knot because the times for which gale-force winds continue is relatively short compared with the much more extensive time that the lighter winds prevail. The night period is well known for the way the wind over the land goes to sleep for an extended period, so we have to have two hours of full gale-force winds to produce an average 10 kn. speed when the wind has been around 5 kn. for 16 hours. Now gale durations are often around an hour or two and do not on average turn up every week. Yet the likelihood of the wind being 5 kn. or so in a week runs into many, many hours. Thus the average speed always seems to be low and much less than you would expect for this reason. Even Den Helder on the Dutch North Sea coast, which statistically is one of the windiest places in the North Sea, can only muster a maximum average speed of 15 kn. Yet from what we have said the reader must now realise that an average 15 kn. means a very high proportion of strong winds.

At sea the wind will only go light if:

(a) the gradient is slack enough, i.e. widely spaced isobars;

(b) if an off-shore wind is opposing the gradient wind as when nocturnal winds blow or when mountain-slope winds oppose on-shore breezes;

(c) if a locally induced thermal wind (due perhaps to a sea temperature gradient) is opposing the pressure gradient.

The effect of the land must never be underestimated. The distance to which land effects stretch is tens of miles and may be more, as for example when local but large-scale winds blow in the Mediterranean or the monsoons set in in the Indian Ocean and elsewhere. Summer winds in the western approaches of the English Channel are statistically more westerly than they should be because of the effect of air rising over the continental land mass and not returning other than by subsidence over the sea.

The diurnal variation in wind speed to which we have become accustomed on land may not appear over the sea. Indeed the wind that blows shoreside and goes quiet over the land will induce a speed-up over the sea to compensate. This coastal sea wind will usually be in evidence in the early morning and will then be overtaken by the growth of wind over the land.

A wind that springs up at any time after a period of near calm is important in any context, but it is particularly important during the evening or night. At this time if you are fully at sea its message is usually that the gradient is strengthening and so you ought to seek advice as to how much it may tighten in the hours ahead. Within the throw of the coast you have to look at the wind's direction. Night winds that start

from landward are usually nocturnal wind, but of course they could be tightening gradient as well. If the offshore wind strengthens to, say, 10 to 15 kn. and there seems no good reason for such a speed (no high ground or mountains backing the coast), you must suspect that the isobars are closing up and perhaps doing so rapidly.

Do not neglect the possibility that local thermal influences due to sea temperatures could be inducing a night wind to blow. The night period cannot have the assistance of convection over the land in creating wind and so any calm or light wind that picks up during this quiet period is a cause for thought. During the day the calm period that suddenly turns into wind may be due to nothing other than convection currents induced by the sun.

The wind of early morning will usually be the lightest of the day, but it should pick up as the day progresses. If after an initial period of strengthening it begins to falter again, you have to ask if there are seabreeze influences at work. Remember that this also means that the wind has to be routed from landward.

It is unusual for the wind to be below the limit of 'light breeze' (6 kn.) in the afternoon near to coasts in summer, but in winter when the sun does not have much heating power the afternoon wind will not be aided by much convection and may well remain light all day. At any time of year the day that remains calm all day is a very rare event. It is almost an impossibility in spring and summer, but it can occur in autumn and winter.

In the afternoon (and that may mean late afternoon) the on-shore seabreeze that has blown through the middle of the day must be expected to go down in strength towards evening. However, if it should falter unnaturally rapidly, consider the prospect that the opposing off-shore wind (which is frustratedly trying to reassert itself somewhere inland) is beginning to push the seabreeze back out to sea. Then the tactic is to work landward to pick up the off-shore wind as soon as it strengthens.

Light wind periods are often the accompaniment of inversion layers not far above the surface. This is certainly true of the light winds of the night period, and if the winds continue light during a fair or sunny day when you feel they should have picked up, then a low inversion is probably the cause.

Such subsidence inversions only appear with well-established anticyclones, and so there should have been a recent history of fair anticyclonic days. In particular if sea-breezes that start do not climb above 4–6 kn. in speed and their throw remains relatively close to the coast, despite a blaze of sunshine you must almost certainly have a strong, low-level, subsidence inversion.

19 MODERATE WINDS

These span the Beaufort scale brackets of Force 4 moderate breeze (11–16 kn.) and Force 5 fresh breeze (17–21 kn.), and so include the speeds that are the best working breezes for almost all craft. At these speeds planing dinghies will plane much of the time however short they are, and longer ones will plane all the time. Larger yachts will be able to carry full canvas and so make maximum way in seas that will not be more than slight to moderate. Sailboarders will have a lot of fun when such wind speeds are directed shoreside.

The diurnal variation in wind speed means that the light wind of the morning will grow to moderate or fresh by the afternoon in inland and coastal regions. If the conditions for seabreezes exist, then the morning that sports a light on-shore wind may well grow into Force 5 by the afternoon, and, in venues like the Mediterranean, Force 6 (22–27 kn.). Fully at sea, it may be that the strongest wind will be found in the hours just before dawn and during the evening, which are also times when showers are most likely over the sea.

In latitudes like those of the English Channel and the North Sea the advent of moderate winds puts the establishment of seabreezes on the borderline. A morning wind that is off-shore and moderate is going to be too strong an adversary for the seabreeze, but the seabreeze forces may well reduce the wind speed offshore* and so lead to a minor form of the anomalous diurnal variation described for the bora on page 139.

If the moderate morning wind is routed sideshore to the major run of the coast and is from the left facing the coast looking from seaward, the seabreeze force can induce winds up to fresh (or even strong) to take a cant in the direction of the land. Thus, when beating, the inshore legs will make more windward way than the offshore ones. If the wind is from the right, the same thing can happen, but it is not going to be so marked. The effect can only be expected to be felt up to a couple of miles out in most cases. Even then we want all those things that make for strong

---

* The word 'offshore' means the sea area offshore, whereas 'off-shore' means the wind direction from land to sea.

breezes: sunshine over the coast and cumulus clouds inland with little or no high cloud to cut down the solar insolation.

If the moderate wind is accompanied by showers, as is very likely in spring, do not be too quick to dismiss the prospect of seabreeze. The spring of 1986 was very cold in the Atlantic Europe area and the sea temperatures were very low (see fig. 16.1). Thus the sunshine that appeared in the mornings of showery days was able to heat the land and induce seabreezes. These cleared the coasts of cloud but built lines of wintery showers inland where the breeze met the northeasterly to northwesterly winds. It was cool on the coast in the wind, but not many miles inland it was snowing (photo 23.1). People to whom I talked about this were surprised that seabreezes happened as early as March and April, but April is the start of the 'big-time' for seabreezes. This month and in May the difference between the power of the sun to heat the land and the low sea temperatures left over from the winter is greatest. Thus in a three-year period that I studied at Thorney Island in Chichester harbour, which is three miles inland from the main run of the English south coast, the average number of days with a recognisable seabreeze in each month was as shown at the foot of this page (Ref. 19).

A most remarkable month was July 1959 when no less than 21 days out of the 31 saw a seabreeze at Thorney, and as I have pointed out there may have been some days when stronger winds confined the seabreeze shifts to simple bendings of the prevailing wind that maybe did not reach inland to any great degree. However, what this list shows is that there is no month when you may not experience a seabreeze because the sun at any time of year can heat the land to above the sea temperature during the middle of

the day. It is only the 'high' months of April to September, however, when we can expect the breeze to influence moderate to strong winds in any great degree.

As well as the influence of the heating of the land on coastal winds it must be remembered that the influence of coastal topography may be felt as much as ten miles away from a coast, and winds that blow along or onshore at a moderate angle to a coast will experience the wind increase we expect when a fluid is confined by solid barriers of some kind or other. Thus the landfall made in a moderate wind probably reaching or even running may run into wind that becomes as much as 10 kn. stronger as the coast is neared. This can happen with quite low coasts, but when the land is relatively high near the shores the constriction effect will be more marked, causing as much as a 15–20 kn. increase and a change in direction to blow more parallel to the coast. However, do not lose sight of the fact that the air does not want to have to do this: it is being forced, and whenever it can find a lower littoral it will be off inland producing more wind cants whose directions can only be divined by looking at the contours and drawing some streamlines.

It is equally well known that winds that blow moderately from some points shorewards will probably drop in speed as the coast sinks astern. This will be at its most marked in the hours from midnight into the dawn period as cold air drains from landward but picks up temperature and becomes convective as it goes seaward.

Moderate winds will normally preclude sea fog, but you cannot unfortunately be sure of this. When the really moist maritime tropical airstreams wing up from southern oceans (or down from northern oceans in the Southern Hemisphere), fog can be borne on winds in the moderate bracket. Visibility

Jan	Feb	March	April	May	June	July	Aug	Sept	Oct	Nov	Dec
2	2	6	9	13	15	14	12	12	5	1	1

may be down to fog limits in other circumstances, e.g. when under the low driving cloudbase of a depression centre, and then such poor visibility may be the accompaniment of strong to gale winds. In extreme winds the visibility may be cut by spume whipped off the top of waves.

Having said all this, more people will be out in moderate winds than almost any others and so their attributes become more important simply because of this fact.

A CHECKLIST ON MODERATE WINDS

The moderate wind you have now or that is forecast can be modified by:

(a)   change in gradient during the period considered;
(b)   time of day (diurnal variation);
(c)   position with respect to coasts;
(d)   seabreeze or nocturnal wind activity;
(e)   showers or thunderstorm down-draughts;
(f)   local sea temperature gradients.

20 OFF A SEABREEZE COAST

The seabreeze systems of the temperate latitudes produce a fairly consistent pattern of behaviour which, once it is appreciated, can make coastwise passage-making easy or can reform tactics when legs of ocean races bring a yacht within the throw of the seabreeze system.

In assessing the likelihood of a seabreeze affecting a coastal belt, ask the following questions:

(1) Is the surface wind strength below 10 kn. around 9 a.m. local time? If it is, then a seabreeze is possible against an off-shore wind.

(2) Is it fair with less than half a cover of low or medium cloud over the land? If it is and the season is spring or summer (but not, usually, autumn), then the sunshine is probably enough to induce a seabreeze. However, allow for the prospect of increasing cloud at medium levels later in the forenoon or afternoon, i.e. check the forecast for signs of coming fronts, etc. The satellite pictures can be useful here if they are screened on an early TV weathercast.

The effect of the seabreeze forces on on-shore winds is to speed them up near the coast and to turn their direction more nearly directly on-shore. Apart from that little can be said. Sideshore winds are more difficult, but if the above criteria are obeyed they will normally swing round to be on-shore by afternoon. It is more likely that sideshore winds from the westerly quadrants will swing progressively into the on-shore direction with time than will ones from the easterly quadrants.

Having said what we can about on-shore and sideshore wind direction, let us return to off-shore early morning winds (fig. 20.1). The wind regime of the seabreeze that sets in against an off-shore wind is complex, but can be understood from fig. 20.2. Read this figure from the top to the bottom. Also remember that the nearer the 9 a.m. wind is to 10 kn. the later the seabreeze will be in establishing itself. So assume that the wind is nearer 5 kn. In fig. 20.2a, by 1100 or 1200 LST (local sun time) a zone of calm has descended on the strip which is 1 to 2 miles offshore. There will be a very light off-shore wind both

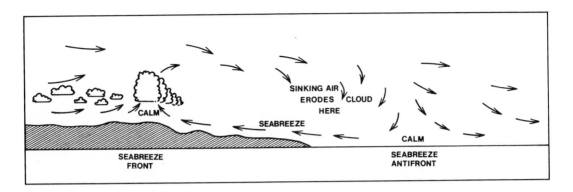

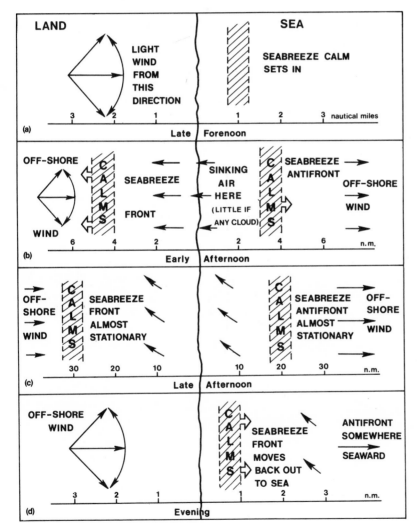

Fig. 20.1 *A seabreeze day when the breeze has pushed in against an off-shore wind. The cloud line of the seabreeze front is some miles inland while the antifront is some miles offshore. Note the off-shore wind to seaward of the antifront and the way the air, sinking to feed the seabreeze current, leads to clear skies over the coastal belt.*

Fig. 20.2 *(a) With a light wind from landward the first signs of seabreeze are calm or fitful patches developing a mile or two off-shore. (b) By early afternoon the situation is rather as depicted in fig. 20.1. (c) Later in the afternoon the seabreeze will have veered very often and the front and antifront have come to rest. Note the changes of horizontal scale. (d) Look for the return of the breeze in the late afternoon or evening, which will blow both front and antifront away out to sea.*

Fig. 20.3   *The nocturnal wind sets in by midnight and continues into the early hours. It is a mixture of land breeze and katabatic wind. The convection over the sea can lead to showers when none is forecast.*

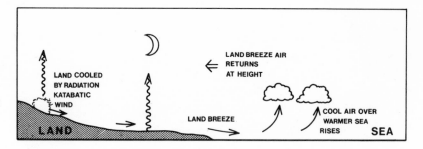

landward and seaward of this zone, increasing as you go further seaward.

By early afternoon (fig. 20.2b) the calm or light-air seabreeze antifront has progressed several miles out to sea while the seabreeze marches inland behind a line of large cumulus clouds. These stretch more or less parallel to the coast and may be seen from seaward especially with the glasses as the seabreeze air descending over the sea evaporates any clouds that might encumber the view. The cloud line is the seabreeze front which is there because the off-shore wind and the on-shore seabreeze must ascend where they meet head on.

By late afternoon (fig. 20.2c) the seabreeze system is running out of puff. The seabreeze front can be anywhere between 20 and 50 miles inland although 30 miles is fairly normal on good seabreeze coasts like those of the south and east coast of England. The seabreeze antifront will be anywhere between 10 and 20 miles offshore and both will induce frustrating calms that usually last through the evening.

Inshore of the antifront the wind will be seabreeze. Its direction is often shifted clockwise by the effect of the Earth's rotation so that southerly on a south-facing coast in the morning is southwesterly by the time the breeze dies. On an east-facing coast the breeze will often swing south-easterly or even southerly as it dies away to nothing with the onset of evening (fig. 20.2d). Unless there has been a change in the gradient during the day, the off-shore

wind will come back during the evening sweeping the calm away, and may be strengthened later by the inverse effect: the land breeze (Ref. 20). Coasts that show seabreeze effects also show landbreeze ones, but there is another factor to be added to the night wind and that is katabatic winds off higher ground inland (fig. 20.3). Together land breeze and katabatic wind make up the total nocturnal wind which, in the absence of any other wind, may amount to 5 kn. within a few miles of a coastline. Further offshore they revert to nothing again. Thus under clear night skies the nearer the coastline the more nocturnal wind there will be (Ref. 19).

Land breeze will be a feature of any coast that is flat or undulating, but katabatics will need hill slopes within twenty or so miles of the coastline, and steeper and higher slopes induce overnight katabatics that may rise to 10 to 20 kn. or more. The most major form of such winds are the downslope winds from inland mountain chains. Off such high coasts we have to expect that the normal change of wind speed through the day (the diurnal variation) will be upset. The tendency for on-shore winds during the late morning can be opposed by downslope winds from cold mountain peaks inland. Obviously one must look for snow-covered tops for this effect to be at its maximum. Then the lowest wind speed will occur during the middle of the day when in normal circumstances it should be maximum. The strongest wind may occur during the early forenoon and the first watch here.

Like all such winds they reach their maximum near the coastline itself and rapidly lose their potency as you go seaward. However, while such downslope winds may favour the night hours, when inland tops are snow-covered they will blow with considerable ferocity at any time of day or night. (See Mistral and Bora in Part Two.)

Having now outlined the usual seabreeze effects we can give a table which will aid the navigator in making the right choices when sailing off a seabreeze coast (table 20.1).

Table 20.1 Guidelines for the navigator when making landfall from well offshore (assuming seabreeze seems possible)[a]

Wind direction	If speed is:	Time of day	Wind experienced	Action
From landward	10 kn. or less (North Atlantic coasts, NA), 15–20 kn. or more in tropics	Late morning through the afternoon (breeze may be up to an hour earlier when from left or right quadrants or directly off-shore)	Gradual loss of wind – could be the antifront. Expect it further offshore the later in the day	Get through it as quickly as possible into the stronger seabreeze inshore. Can you use a tidal set that is going that way?
	15–20 kn. (NA), 20–25 kn. (tropics)	Should be no real effect in forenoon. Possible during afternoon and early evening	Antifront will be further inshore when morning wind stronger and it may get swept away at any time	Wind may be fickle but usually there will be some. Allow for seabreeze being blown away, especially late afternoon
On-shore – steady	10 kn. or less	Late afternoon or early evening	You have reason to believe that the wind is seabreeze. So you must expect a return to gradient wind soon. Coming from further offshore you could have had an antifront calm earlier. Look for signs of cloud edge or haze wall coming from landward. You may be able to find the gradient direction from any Cu that may be about over the sea	If wind is dying, work shorewards to meet new stronger wind. How you insert into it is for the tactician. Once you have it you can expect it to stay and strengthen somewhat

continued

Table 20.1 *continued*

Wind direction	If speed is:	Time of day	Wind experienced	Action
Off-shore	15–20 kn. (temperate latitudes), 20–25 kn. (tropics)	Any time	The strongest seabreeze days and coasts are needed to stop and reverse these winds. However, allow for times when slackening gradient makes for wind decrease during day. Then late afternoon breeze can occur near coast but may only be reflected in some awkward wind-shifts offshore	Expect problems the nearer you get to the coastline. Any signs of lightening strength mean seabreeze is working
On-shore	More than 10 kn.	Morning	Increase in convection over land (especially if showers or storms break out) can enhance on-shore wind and may shift its direction closer to directly onshore near the coast. Little effect further offshore. Could become fresh or even strong	Can confidently expect to have wind during whole period. Direction should also stay fairly constant

[a] Think about the possible growth of showers over the land in the summer half of the year which tends to kill the breeze inshore and has a knock-on effect further offshore. If thunderstorms are forecast, the breeze can be lost early and replaced by a moderate to strong wind from landward. Shoreside winds on south- and east-facing coasts, which come from the left facing onshore, usually swing progressively to seabreeze direction. When they come from the right the swing occurs, but it is much slower and may be more erratic. The off-shore antifront may not be present. On north-facing coasts west winds increase under seabreeze influence and turn on-shore later than on south- or east-facing coasts. On west-facing coasts seabreezes occur late in the forenoon or early afternoon on the coast and may hang on into the evening while sun stays out on the land. Winds, stronger than you would expect to be influenced, can be canted shorewards well inshore despite blowing strongly shoreside further offshore.

21 TROPICAL METEOROLOGY

As far as met. goes, we are in the 'tropics' when the hold that the geostrophic force has on the wind becomes so loose as to be meaningless. To understand this read the heading 'Gradient wind' in Part Two. It will be evident from what is said there that once you have selected an isobaric interval (such as 4 mb between isobars) and assuming you neglect changes in air density, the product

$D \times \sin \phi$ is a constant quantity

where D is the isobaric spacing and ϕ is the latitude.

So in low latitudes the value of D must increase and will become infinite at the equator. In other words there is no such thing as Buys Ballot's law near the equator (see Part Two). Winds in that region simply blow from where pressure is higher straight into where it is lower. There are no dartboards of isobars enclosing low centres and moving in the way we are used to in the temperate latitudes. Low-latitude charts will have widely spaced isobaric patterns simply because the isobaric interval chosen for the chart must lead to a much slacker gradient in order to balance the very small geostrophic force for any given wind speed.

In fig. 21.1 the spacing for latitudes from 60°N or S to 10°N or S are compared for a 4 mb isobaric spacing. This shows why isobars become almost non-existent as we traverse 10°N or S latitude. This band of 20 degrees that spans the equator is the realm of the equatorial low and it is fed with the north-east trades on the northern side of the equator and similarly by the south-east trades on the southern side. If air converges on the equator in this way, then there is only one avenue of escape and that is upwards. The convergence zone is marked by the Intertropical Convergence Zone (ITCZ) (sometimes called the inter-tropical front). The title ITCZ is now preferred as the characteristics are not anything like a front and the zone is one of heavy rains and thunderstorms. The equatorial thunderstorms are the means by which the electric field of the whole Earth is neutralised, and so they are a more or less continuous phenomenon within the zone. However, as the same ITCZ also contains the once-dreaded doldrums, it is not the right concept to imagine a continuous ring

Fig. 21.1 *The isobar spacing on a map of given scale increases dramatically as you move towards the equator, and at the equator it is theoretically infinite.*

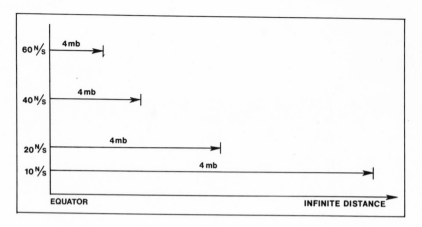

of massive thunderstorms girdling the equatorial regions. The ITCZ migrates somewhat with the sun, being mainly north of the equator in the summer of the Northern Hemisphere and south of the equator during the summer of the Southern Hemisphere. Its movement is not marked over the oceans, but can be very large over the landmasses.

Because of the nature of the ITCZ it is best to consider it as a region where very local and often short-lived storm areas occur and one where the weather situation will change from day to day without any noticeable change in other conditions. It is a very volatile and unpredictable region. For this reason the charts that are drawn to include the equatorial region are drawn showing the winds that either exist or are expected to exist a relatively short time in the future. There is no such thing as a six-day forecast for this region – or even a two-day one.

The form of chart that can make sense as we span the equatorial zone is a map of streamlines. Streamlines are not isobars. They follow the paths of tubes of air which may be wide or narrow and which do not have a relation to wind speed through their spacing. The form of chart issued by Naveastocean, Norfolk, Va, includes streamlines (solid lines in fig. 21.2) and

isotachs (dashed lines) which are lines of equal wind speed. There are also individual observations of wind speed from ships, balloons and satellites within the 'boundary layer', i.e. the first 2000 ft deck of the atmosphere.

Yachts planning to enter or traverse the equatorial regions will only be able to keep fully abreast of the wind and weather through a constant monitoring of the available forecasts, and it is here perhaps more than anywhere else that facsimile comes into its own. For example, the ITCZ can often be seen on the whole-earth images from geostationary satellites which are of necessity sitting over the equator, and this supplements the output of charts which may only give winds.

It cannot be too strongly emphasised that the crossed-winds technique for personal forecasting cannot possibly work in low latitudes, and one should not rely on it below, say, 30° N or S. If you want to know what the upper wind situation is over the tropics, then charts are issued of winds around 200 mb by stations such as Naveastocean and these come from satellites looking at the motion of cirrus cloud, radar wind observations of radiosonde and other balloons as well as aircraft. A typical tropical pressure/wind analysis is shown in fig. 21.3. This covers the Caribbean and

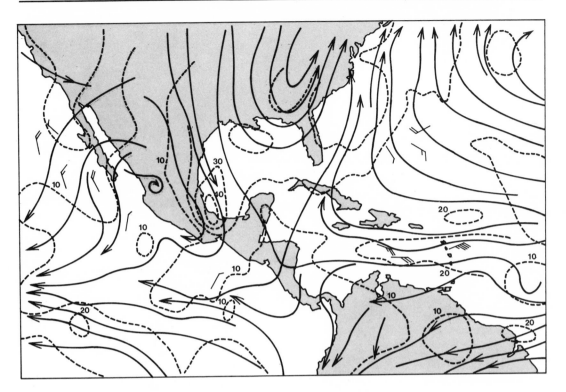

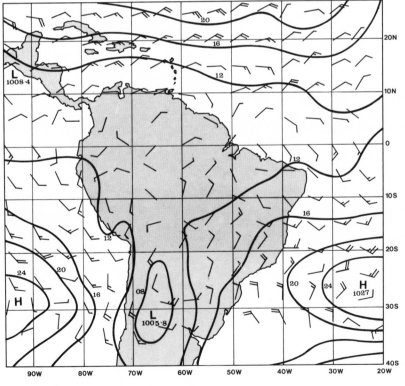

Fig. 21.2   *(above) Because the normal relationship between pressure and wind has broken down, the met. services resort to boundary layer and other analyses. By the boundary layer they mean the lowest 2000 ft of the atmosphere. The solid lines are streamlines, and the dashed lines are isotachs – lines of equal wind speed. The closed '40' isotach over Veracruz, southern Mexico, means that a local area of gale-force winds exists there.*

Fig. 21.3   *Isobars and winds for the tropics for midday, 12 November. Low centres have their pressures given to the nearest decimal point of a millibar because small changes in barometric height have a profound effect on weather in the tropics.*

South America down to 40°S. Note the fact that there are no isobars over most of the equatorial belt. Also it is only some 40 days off midsummer's day in the Southern Hemisphere.

Weather in the tropics is impossible to describe in detail in a book of this size. The best advice is to obtain and read the Pilot for the coasts you intend to sail. There you will also find the information on tropical revolving storms and how best to avoid them. Tracking the progress of such storms was one of the first spin-offs from satellite observations. Prior to the satellite era their breeding grounds were lacking in observations, but now the development and progress of each storm can be followed from its inception through the continuous monitoring by geostationary satellites. They never form in the equatorial band 5°S to 5°N nor near coasts, and the sea temperature needs to be above 27°C. They gain their energy and fuel (water vapour) from the warm seas, and once they drift inland they spend their energies in a couple of days. However, old hurricanes must not be forgotten as they cross the Atlantic in the later months of the season. A considerable number survive as depressions which very

often seem to rejuvenate on approaching European shores. In their circulations there will sometimes be strong winds and, in some notorious cases, hurricane-force winds. Electric storms and a generally tropical look and feel to the weather go with the passage of these old hurricanes.

Before leaving this brief introduction to tropical met. it is worth looking at how a major fax station which covers the equator solves the problem of winds, clouds, etc. in this region. An analysis from San Francisco is shown in fig. 21.4. It is late in the hurricane season, being 31 October 1985 and as the name Xina tells us. From the satellite images the cloud belts are identified. For example we have scattered, isolated clouds even associated with the low at 25°N while Xina is a compact little Michelin-man of cloud travelling east at 7 kn. The general wind directions are shown by the arrows and the wind speeds by the barbs on the wind arrows. As this is an 'analysis', it is an actual chart for this time and will need backing up with some kind of a forecast chart to see how things will develop. However, from a yachting point of view there is a great concentration on surface wind in tropical weather charts.

Fig. 21.4   *The Pacific side of tropical America is shown by streamlines, wind arrows and cloud. The tropical storm Xina is moving at 7 kn. towards Mexico. (As received from San Francisco fax.)*

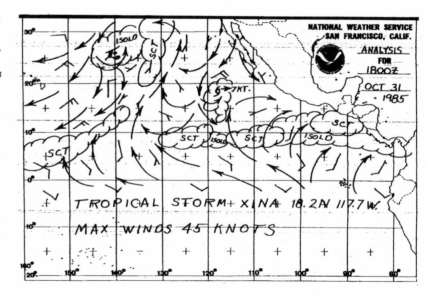

22   THUNDERSTORMS

Storms can occur almost anywhere, but some places are more prone to them than others. Inland areas not too far from the sea are the best breeding grounds. Coastal areas in Europe do not see many storms but this is not true of the Mediterranean and the United States (as fig. 22.2 shows). In England there is a region around and to the north of London which shows a higher incidence of storms than elsewhere, and the numbers fall off outwards from this centre with relatively small numbers in the west and in Scotland. In Europe regions such as the North German Plain are very prone to storms, but such areas cannot be fully catalogued here.

When heavy thunderstorms occur over coastal regions it is because they have generated inland and drifted out over the coast (photo C.19). Thus it is most likely that they will turn up in the late afternoons and evenings, going on into the night. In more tropical areas there is often a clear morning near coasts and islands followed by the development of storms over the land during the middle of the day.

Wind tends to blow in to feed the storms in their early stages so that coastal onshore breezes that increase for no apparent reason should make you think of thunder inland if the conditions seem to warrant it. Sea-breezes feed storms that might otherwise not have occurred. In the satellite cloud picture which is photo 23.1, parts of the coastal strip of East Anglia are clear of cloud, but storms are being set off by seabreeze activity along a seabreeze front further inland.

Once the storms have developed, then their role as inverters of the atmosphere comes into play and cold damp air is cascaded on to the surface by falling rain and hail. It is accompanied by heavy squalls which may increase the wind to 30–40 kn. temporarily and in the worst cases gusts of 50–60 kn. may occur. Yachts meeting storm areas cannot escape them so they should shorten sail while they can and before the arch-cloud which projects out ahead of the storm arrives overhead. The cold air 'nose' where the big wind occurs is either under the arch or out ahead of it (fig. 22.1).

It is the wind that is the element most

Fig. 22.1 *The anatomy of a big thunderstorm. Times and distances are gauged from when the nose of the big squall reaches you.*

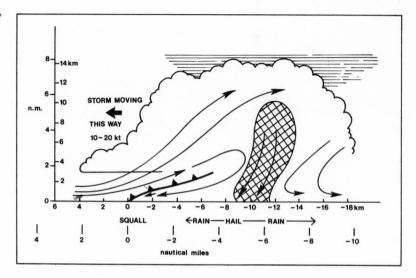

likely to produce a hazard for yachts at sea, especially as the contrast between the light, often sultry conditions before the storm and the gale-force winds, coolness and heavy precipitation that follow is so damaging to crew morale. However, it is rare for yachts at sea to be struck by lightning, and in a lifetime of lecturing to yachtsmen I have only met a handful of people who have been struck themselves or know of others who were struck.

It is far more likely that a yacht will be struck in the marina or at moorings than at sea, if for no other reason than that storms tend to hug coasts and not extend far over the sea. However, this does not apply to narrow waters such as the English Channel where storms bred over France are a regular feature of weather in the Channel and southern England generally.

It must be realised that storms differ. For example, there are isolated storms that give a rumble of thunder and are gone when the weather is very bad and winds are high. These indicate the passage of a cold front and also show that the air is very unstable so heavy showers are likely to follow.

Such individual storm cells may become more numerous, for example in spring when cold polar air finds itself over warm land, but they will, like those above, come under the heading of airmass thunderstorms. These are just big showers with some thunder and hail thrown in for good measure (photo C.19).

The storms mentioned above as being bred over France and then invading England are an example of a second form of thundery outbreak (photo C.24). These are high-level storms which have the characteristics of unstable warm fronts. The cloud bases may be as much as 10 000 ft up, and therefore the lightning, while spectacular, is largely from cloud to cloud at altitude and so not dangerous. However, the occasional bolt to earth needs a more than usually big build-up of charge and thus, if it strikes anything, it is more than usually disruptive. The thunder from these frontal storms peals around the sky through the sounding board of the clouds, but such thunder is obviously not very near. Those who have been close to a lightning bolt know that there is just one big bang without the reverberations we associate with a clap of thunder. Another similar, but less intense, form of the above is called thundery showers. Here showers occur from medium-level cloud and are accompanied by thunder. Wind associated with such storms cannot be very strong, as to become organised with updraughts and downdraughts the storm cells must not be torn apart in the vertical wind shear.

The entity we call a thunderstorm is the amalgamation of a large number of storm cells, and these need several important ingredients. We need heat, a trend to low pressure, moist air to feed the updraughts, and a more than usually cold upper air so that convection can go on to great altitude. Stagnant cols are favourite breeding grounds for summer thunderstorms, but anywhere inland that has got hot during the morning can experience a 'heat low' due to more air flowing out of the column over the low than is flowing into it. The result is the creation of one or more storm cells that will breed others near them and so keep the storm going as well as spreading it over a wider area. Such large storms come up against the wind. It is a wind that they themselves are forming by drawing the hot humid air from ahead to feed their updraughts. This pre-storm wind blows up over the heavy, cold outflow where wind directions tend to reverse.

The anatomy of the large storm (fig. 22.1) shows how the cold squall that comes from the direction of the storm is often well ahead of the rain and nowhere near the heavy hail which may be five miles away. The squall may advance ahead of the edge of the arch-cloud or be just below it. You have to keep an eye on the water to see when it is going to hit you. The hail from these storms is of normal size, and although it may be deposited to some depth on deck it will tend to be a slush of ice pellets and no real hazard.

There is, however, a different beast that turns up occasionally and this is called a 'supercell' storm. Hail from these monsters may be as large as tennis balls and irregular in shape so that bombardment with the ice lumps causes damage to persons and property. Luckily they are rare, their incidence in England being about once every twenty years. However, in areas more prone to storms they can be more frequent.

Together with storms go tornadoes over land which become tornado storm spouts over the water and are more dangerous than simple water spouts that occur fairly frequently. Water spouts occur in places as widely spaced as the English Channel and the Mediterranean, and in the latter area spouts can be induced when the air is too dry to form cloud above them. Generally tornadoes are products of inland areas and are very rare in coastal districts. However, there is a form of cloud called 'mamma' which is a set of domed downward-projecting cloud elements formed on the edges of thunderstorms. Once seen these are not easily forgotten and in the United States they are recognised as a sign that tornadoes could be in the offing (photo C.20).

Weather radar chains keep tabs on the development and movement of storm areas because rain (and especially heavy rain or hail) gives good echoes although clouds are too tenuous to do so. Radar summaries are broadcast on fax and will resemble fig. 22.2, which shows the echoes on a day in July over the United States. When it is suspected that storm areas exist in your vicinity, you can obtain information on their movements from the weather bureaux who will be in touch with the radar networks. When it is expected that cloud-burst conditions are already in being or are about to break out, warnings may be given over the domestic radio. (See Radar in Part Two.)

Another form of detection system has been in use for many years and is known as SFERIC. The crackling on the radio that perhaps first warns you of lightning occurring somewhere not too far away can be

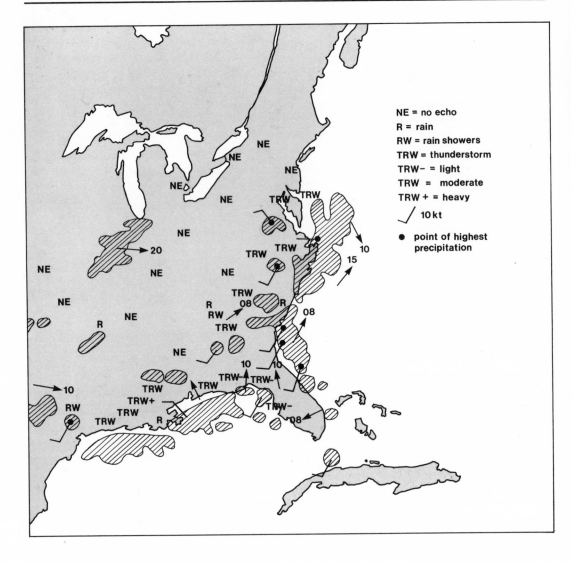

NE = no echo
R = rain
RW = rain showers
TRW = thunderstorm
TRW− = light
TRW = moderate
TRW + = heavy
/ 10 kt
● point of highest
  precipitation

located by special radio equipment, and the 'cocked-hat' from three stations can locate the position of the lightning discharges. Stations in Britain and its surroundings can locate and pinpoint storms as far afield as the Mediterranean.

Fig. 22.2 *Areas of thunderstorms and showers as seen by radar over the United States and broadcast by fax.*

23 SATELLITE CLOUD IMAGES

It has to be said at the outset that the uses to which satellite cloud images can be put by the yachtsman are limited. There is a great vogue for screening these images on the TV but only the vaguest of meanings can be read into the pictures.

The satellites are of two kinds. First, the Earth is ringed round the equator with five geostationary satellites which between them can keep tabs on the whole world's clouds. These satellites are 36 000 miles up, and as an example the European one, Meteosat, sits on the Greenwich meridian where it crosses the equator. The American one that picks up the early development of hurricanes is GOES-E and is on longitude 75°W. In the latitudes of northern Europe and Canada the curvature of the Earth foreshortens the cloud images, but electronic processing can allow for this and the images broadcast by Offenbach fax appear as if one is sitting over, say, the North Sea rather than the equator.

Secondly there are the polar orbiting satellites which you can imagine rotating round a giant cartwheel surrounding the Earth. The wheel stays fixed in space, i.e. it does not change its position with respect to the Sun. The Earth, however, spins inside the wheel and so the polar orbiters see all parts of the globe twice a day. These TIROS satellites are closer to the Earth than the geostationary ones and can perform many tasks other than the main ones of imaging cloud patterns in the visible region by day and night and in the infra-red by night. For these tasks they use a very complex advanced high-resolution radiometer (AVRR) which allows monitoring of ice coverage, measurement of the Earth's heat flux and of sea surface temperatures, and assessment of the degree to which snow and ice are melting or forming. In addition there is a microwave sounding unit that can see through clouds, and a stratospheric sounding unit that can assess temperatures and winds in the stratosphere. (See Satellites in Part Two.)

Recipients can use APT (automatic picture transmission) equipment which will interrogate the satellite when it is within range and print out the received images. More advanced equipment allows for high-resolution picture transmission (HRPT)

23.1   It is spring and the sea is cold while the land is warm. So the land stands out stark against the sea. The remains of a front trailing back from the old occluded depression between Scotland and Norway is the catalyst for heavy and wintry showers over the southern half of England. Over France fleets of cumulus form along the wind while the same heavy showers have developed over the Manche coasts and Brittany.

where the detail becomes much more obvious. On the whole two objects which are under half a kilometre apart cannot be seen as separate by TIROS, but that is five times better than from the geostationary satellites which are so much higher up.

Having given an introduction to the satellites we need to pick out what can and what cannot be of use to the yachtsman. The images see the tops of clouds and those clouds are in direct sunlight. Thus ice-crystal clouds (cirriform) will reflect very strongly and will dominate the pictures. From the ground a cirrus layer may appear very tenuous, but with the sun shining on it from above it will be a sheet of brilliant white. On the other hand clouds, which from the ground look very solid and obvious, may easily be lost in the satellite image. The IR images are on a grey scale that makes colder whiter and warmer darker. Thus in spring, when sea temperatures are cold and the land warm by day, the land areas stand out stark against a light sea (photo 23.1). In autumn, when sea and land tend to be the same temperature, there is little contrast and the land tends to be lost in the sea. In the depths of winter the cold land looks light against a darker (warmer) sea. Equally snow surfaces become white as do ice floes, and the coldest of all will be the cirrus clouds.

For this reason fronts and depressions make the most obvious objects on the satellite images. The images show the meteorologists where depressions and their fronts are over sea wastes where no ships ply. They indicate the early stages in the birth of new depressions and show gaps in the cloud shields over lows which might otherwise not be seen. However, the whitest areas of cloud cover the worst surface weather and it takes some mental agility to translate the whiteness of cirrus (whiteness tends to be associated in the surface observer's mind with fair weather) into the nimbostratus and rain or snow that will be underneath and invisible (fig. 23.1).

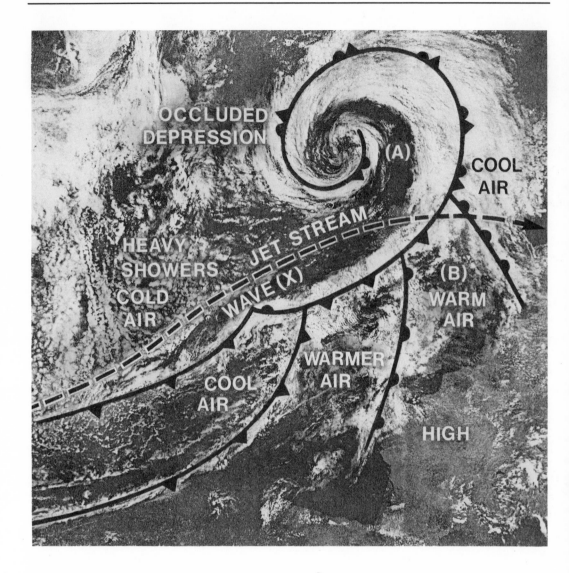

OCCLUDED
DEPRESSION
(A)
COOL
AIR
HEAVY
SHOWERS   JET STREAM
COLD   WAVE (X)
AIR
COOL
AIR
WARMER
AIR
(B)
WARM
AIR
HIGH

Fig. 23.1 *When we add the surface fronts and the jet to a satellite image we begin to see what lies under the virgin whiteness – a nasty lot of surface weather.*

The showery airstreams are revealed very well by the satellite images as they look either like a wandering flock of sheep or, when less well developed, like skeins of rather imperfect lace. You can gain a good idea of whether the air behind a front to come will be full of showers or not by noting if the cumulonimbus 'sheep' are being driven down behind it. (North-west of Ireland in photo 23.1.)

Other lower clouds will have to be searched for as they are darker and less easy to spot. If you have fax, then the significant weather charts will show the kind of cloud expected. Some stations broadcast interpretations of the cloud images called nephanalyses (see Part Two), and those who wish to interpret the pictures for themselves will have to compare the nephanalysis with the parent image to learn what each cloud form looks like from space.

It is perhaps in the observation of hurricanes that the satellites have scored the greatest success and paid for their keep. Once the development areas were ones where no ships plied and so hurricanes were well developed before they could be spotted. Now the track of every hurricane is known accurately as it is followed hour by hour from the GOES-E satellite. The Japanese GMS over 140°E does the same for the development of typhoons, and the Russian GOMS over 70°E follows the Indian Ocean cyclones. The Japanese satellite will also see the Willy-Willies that invade the north coasts of Australia.

The great loss of life that used to accompany the onset of hurricanes in the Caribbean, the Gulf and the East Coast of the United States has been greatly mitigated by the timely warnings now given. Hurricane Diana forced the evacuation of 100 000 people from the coastal regions of North and South Carolina in mid-September 1984. Yet only two people were killed as a result of the hurricane, whose winds touched 120 kn. near its centre, and 90 kn. winds raised the sea level by 10 ft on some coasts. However, even the yacht that has fax and can follow the hurricanes from the images that are broadcast must still listen to the advisories and act accordingly. The met. services know more about it than you will in these circumstances.

Old hurricanes that invade the European theatre have been referred to elsewhere (page 170) and in photo R.10 we see old Hurricane Flossie moving across the North Sea on 16 September 1978. Both Flossie and the occluded depression in photo 23.1 show the same characteristic swirling motion in their high clouds and fleets of showers on their western sides.

With sea fog such a hazard, and especially one of the sailing season, it is an important attribute of satellite pictures that they show up where the fog is. Once it was impossible to tell how extensive or how patchy sea fog was. Even now the warmth of fog layers may make them very difficult to spot against the sea surface, but photo R.9 shows the kind of help in finding fog that TIROS-N gives. As this is May, the fog burns off over land and for this reason it seems to fill waterways such as the Bristol Channel.

A complex and spectacular depression and frontal system covered Europe on 6 August 1979. The surface fronts and features have been added to show what lies below the clouds (fig. 23.1). Great spirals are eye-catching but they indicate old systems. The clouds only get like this when a depression has been occluding for a long time, but it explains how sometimes the cloud clears only to close in again later. This is what would have happened north of Scotland (A). Over the North Sea we have an open warm sector (B). Conditions would be warm and humid there. However, the most interesting feature is perhaps the most innocuous. It is the little hump on the cold front which is a wave depression. It will be moving north-east fairly rapidly and so a yachtsman near X who sees the cold-front cloud clearing will very soon find the sky closing in again with cyclonic wind-shifts and rain breaking out.

It can be inferred that the jet stream lies somewhere as shown and so the wave could develop as it is in the right configuration with the jet. However, it does not appear to have enough room to become a full-blooded depression. Another clue lies in the 'wig' of Cb clouds that exist to the north-west. They indicate cold air over warmer sea, and cold air in juxtaposition with warm air on the other side of the front could be the means of making such a wave low develop.

Before satellites revealed them to us no one would have dreamed up so complex a set of fronts as the image shows. It is difficult to know how this system got the way it did. However, the frontal ideas still apply. Cool air over Scandinavia is separated from warm air over the North Sea by a warm front and from warmer air over the south-west approaches by another warm front. Then a cold front introduces cool air before the final cold front brings in cold air.

24 A PATTERN FOR PERSONAL FORECASTING

To do your own forecasting and make it a practical exercise you must establish a pattern of thought. The following should help suggest what you ought to be thinking about, although it need not necessarily be the order in which you think about it. It depends on how much of the history of the recent weather you know and what you have already done to gain knowledge of the developing situation. So it depends on your state of knowledge and experience and often on how long you have been in this locality and learned its idiosyncrasies. First you should:

Establish the type of airstream. There are three states of the lowest deck of the atmosphere – what we call the boundary layer. They are stable, unstable and neutral. The latter is often transitory as stability changes to instability and vice versa, so we will concentrate on the other two.

On the whole, warm airstreams will be stable and cool ones unstable. However, there are many exceptions to this rule. Over land with fair conditions the diurnal variation in temperature will have air going from stable overnight through neutral to unstable by day and then back again. It is relative temperature between surface and air that matters. Warmth generated in surface air parcels will seek cooler air above, and air above will come down to take its place. This leads to mixing, but mixing leads to significant micro-wind-shifts for yachts.

Unstable air will be variable in the short term, but the variations will be less between land and sea than in the case of stable air. Stable air is capable of being very different from what the isobars say it should be, whereas unstable air cannot differ. Unstable air will ignore the influence of topography much more than stable air will. In fact stable air tends to be land-hugging, and so overnight winds are more likely to follow the dictates of the land.

Unstable air generates cumulus and cumulonimbus which, being lumpy skies, lead to lumpy wind with many recurrent wind-shifts. However, these are only on the scale of minutes. Stable airstreams tend to make more permanent shifts or stay where they are for long periods, and this applies very much to the early hours of the morning.

Fog is impossible in unstable airstreams, but becomes a risk as soon as stability sets in so the chances of fog vary with the kind of airstream, and when fronts pass, so the airmass changes its characteristics and each frontal change has to be considered on its attributes. You need some information from stations on the other side of the front.

Consider possible changes. Here the operative word is 'possible' because we have just mentioned one circumstance where fog is impossible. It is as useful to think of what could not happen as what might happen. For example in chapter 20, 'Off a Sea-breeze Coast', it is suggested that once the wind speed is above 15 kn. from the land there will be no possibility of an on-shore breeze developing. We have to make the proviso that this means Atlantic Europe and similar coasts and does not apply to 'hot' coasts like some in the Mediterranean and the Gulf of Mexico, etc. So as long as we keep such a wind, seabreeze is out, but a lowering of wind speed could be in. Here you must consult the various tables designed to help you make decisions about the possibilities, and only you on the spot can possibly make them.

The wind veers with height when a warmer airmass is in the offing and backs with height when a colder one is approaching (NH). This is the essence of our crossed-winds rules and gives intelligence that an unstable airstream is going to stabilise or a stable one to become more unstable. Time of day or temperatures of surface and air do not make it certain that there will be a change of stability, but it should be considered together with its implications.

Weather worsens under cyclonic and improves under anticyclonic curvature of the isobars. Only rarely are isobars straight and their continual writhings about lead to deteriorations and improvements which may be minor or major. Falling barometric pressure indicates a more cyclonic situation and so the highest

chance of a backing wind (NH). Looked at another way, increasing high and/or medium cloud will often be accompanied by a backing wind. (In SH read veering.) Conversely a rising barometer or clearing upper skies are very likely to be associated with a veer. Thus sky signs, even without barometric changes to back them up, can indicate long-term wind-shifts.

Short forecast soon past. This bit of weather lore has another line, 'Long foretold long hold', which contains the same message. Take the time between first seeing cirrus and when the sun disappears behind the murk and expect that to be about the same as the time from the loss of the sun to when the warm front or occlusion clears. Get a sky like photo C.7 and because most of the pre-frontal clouds are in the sky at once you can expect a quick clearance. When photo C.1 takes hours to become photo C.12, then you are dealing with a much more extensive – and probably vicious – system.

If the wind gets up very rapidly, then it is likely to be a short, sharp blow. Most strong winds take over six hours to grow from Force 4 to a Force 7 or 8 gale (Ref. 19).

Intensity time tends to be constant. In other words the small wave low that ripples up a cold front is not intense and so passes quickly. The low that deepens tends to slow and when it stops deepening it tends to move again. A very deep low uses its energy to deepen and not to move. The squall as the ana-cold front whips through is another example of the rule. It sometimes occurs that a bad weather system can be intense and also move, but such cases are rare.

Or take the summer thunderstorm. The rain and hail while they last are very intense, but they only last a short time whereas the warm front rains solidly for hours but not with any great gusto. Thus the result of both is about the same quantity of rain. Thus we get most of our summer rain from cumulonimbus and most of the winter precipitation from nimbostratus.

Strong weather derives from strong temperature contrast. This means strong temperature contrast in the airmasses that are in juxtaposition in the frontal structure of a depression. That may not be so evident on the ground as it will be aloft. The true character of an airmass only reveals itself above the boundary layer because mixing feeds the lowest layers of air with the attributes of the surface over which it has moved. In other words it becomes modified and altered – sometimes out of recognition.

However, with young warm and cold airmasses set side by side the jet stream becomes hurricane force and the whole structure of the depression becomes charged with energy so that surface winds grow to gale or severe gale and the fronts that pass are very active.

On a smaller scale, cold upper air over a warm surface grows the atmospheric explosions we call thunderstorms. Here the contrast is in the vertical, but it still leads to severe weather.

Ascending air breeds weather. We need not say much about this. What has been said in many places throughout this book makes the principle quite evident.

Descending air erodes weather. Whereas the ascending air mentioned above must start low down, the descending air of this principle starts high up. Thus its effects are less likely to be noticed. At best skies are totally cloudless.

What goes up must come down. This involves the principle that nature abhors a vacuum. If a warm air parcel lifts off (a thermal), then air has to sink round it to make up for the loss at the surface. If you get a trough in an airstream, then more air is ascending in it

than is descending so ahead and behind the trough more air must descend than ascends and skies will clear. If you get a heat low over the land during the day, you have to have a high over the adjacent water to compensate. The examples are endless.

Weather moves in a continuous manner. The idea of continuity is important as you follow a low or a high, a front or a trough from chart to chart. It is in front of our eyes whenever we see time-lapse sequences of geostationary satellite pictures moving across our TV screens. If you can, keep a continuity chart for the centres of low and high pressure you know are in being. Move on the fronts with them using ideas given under Fronts in Part Two.

Wind starts for a reason. When from light conditions the wind begins to pick up there is a physical reason. Wind cannot blow for no reason and you have to ask what the reason is. It is particularly important to ask why a night wind is starting, as thermal reasons for wind are much less in evidence at night. The exceptions are nocturnal winds from land to sea, but they are not of themselves above light to moderate. Winds start for many reasons, but is yours due perhaps to the breaking of an inversion letting stronger wind from above arrive at the surface, or is it due to increasing gradient? If the latter, you need a forecast as to how far the wind increase is expected to go.

In the above I have tried to suggest some modes of thought that may help the non-meteorologist formulate questions to which he can then seek answers. Yet no matter how many aids you have, electronic or otherwise, there is always going to be room for oceans of doubt and indecision as to the next move, because luckily the sailing game is like that.

Part Two

Use this section to find more technical
detail on topics mentioned in Part One, and
as a form of index in which to look up
words and phrases.

EXPLANATIONS OF WEATHER WORDS AND PHRASES

Adiabatic is a term used to describe the cooling or heating of air parcels as they ascend or descend. Literally an adiabatic change is one that takes place without heat entering or leaving the air parcel. See **Lapse rates** and **Latent heat**.

Advection is a term implying horizontal transport of a weather element from place to place as opposed to vertical transport as occurs in convection. Examples include advection fog which may invade an area when warmer, moister air is advected over a cooler surface, or the advection of smoke haze from an industrial area.

Airmasses originate in source regions which have extreme characteristics. They are either cold and very wet (polar or arctic Maritime airmasses), very warm and wet (tropical Maritime), very warm and dry (tropical Continental) or very cold and dry (polar Continental). Each of these source regions is the seat of a semi-permanent anticyclone, and where the regions are can be seen in fig. AR.1.

Airmasses that come straight out of their source region stable can retain their extreme characteristics, but most airmasses are already modified and are dryer or wetter, warmer or colder than when they started. A good example is returning maritime Polar (rmP) air in Europe which only grows small fair-weather cumulus clouds, but which was once full of big shower clouds. This is due to its modification as it has come on a very long sea track around the Icelandic low-pressure area.

Recognising the kind of airmass you are in is a first requisite for forecasting the weather to come, and so a 'Think-tank' on air masses follows (table A.1). Note that in fig. AR.1 the abbreviations may be followed by a 'k' for colder than underlying surface, or by a 'w' for warmer. Thus k = unstable air with showers, gusts, variable winds, etc., and w = stable with risk of fog, low cloud, drizzle, etc.

Alto clouds are of the middle reaches of the atmosphere and are very much associated with fronts that have formed, are forming or are dispersing (photo R.1). They are also harbingers of thunder. Alto-cumulus (Ac) consists of globular masses

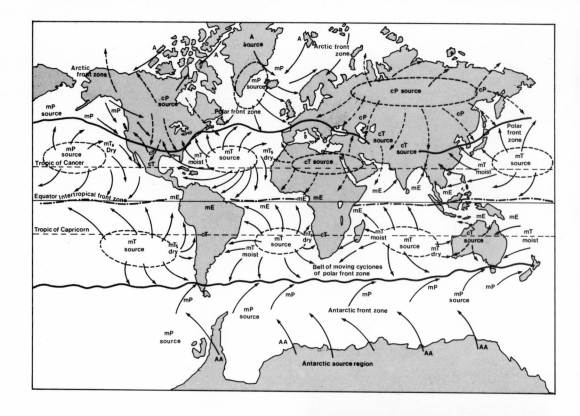

Fig. AR.1   *The airmasses of the world and their source regions. On this diagram rmP is not indicated, but comes out of the Atlantic from the mP source region on a long track round the Icelandic low.*
Key: mT = maritime Tropical;
mT$_s$ = maritime Tropical subsiding;
mE = maritime Equatorial;
mP = maritime Polar;
cP = continental Polar;
cT = continental Tropical; A = Arctic;
AA = Antarctic.

R.1   *Alto-cumulus in dapples and waves at the top of the picture gives way to altostratus at the bottom. This is typical of older warm fronts or occlusions and the cloud is advancing from bottom right to top left.*

Table A.1 A 'think-tank' on airmasses

Airmass type	Recent history	Think about:
mT, maritime Tropical (pure) (cloudy, muggy, wet)	Cyclonic, changeable	Fog, low stratus, hill fog, drizzle, orographic rain – a cold front to come
maritime Tropical (drying out)	A day or so since true cyclonic weather passed. Wind sticks doggedly to same quarter	Retaining this airstream because of developments taking place westwards, e.g. cold front carried away by ridge development or low stuck to the west
mP, maritime Polar (pure) (well-washed airstream, heap clouds, cool)	Cyclonic changeable	Showers at all times over sea. Showers by day, clear skies by night over land. Heavy showers on windward high ground. Fewer showers in shadowed areas. Fog patches and frost inland
mP, maritime Polar (subsiding) (good visibility but showers are inhibited)	Showers die out, considerable cloudiness perhaps, particularly if showers die out over land by day	Next warm front and depression; or barometer steadily rising for a good ridge. Heat in summer – perhaps storms
rmP, returning maritime Polar	Wind from rmP quarter, usually W (NH) or E (SH) perhaps for some considerable time. Fair conditions	Seabreezes and land breezes, mountain and valley winds. Fog and frost hollows
cT, continental Tropical (dry, warm)	Establishment of wind from a cT quarter	Heatwaves, sluggish sea and land breezes. When will thunderstorms break it down?
cP, continental Polar	Establishment of wind from a cP quarter	Is sea warm enough and fetch long enough (about 500 miles) to set off showers? Extreme cold in winter
Arctic (NH) or Antarctic (SH)	Establishment of wind direct from arctic source region	Extreme cold whether on sea or land track. Polar lows when on exclusively sea track
Equatorial (wet in depth, prone to thunderstorms)	Air from cells established in the ITCZ – 15°N or S of equator	Light and variable winds – a doldrum area – much convection cloud

arranged in groups, lines or waves. It sometimes shows small coloured patches (irisations) that are due to refraction through small water droplets (photo C.13). This distinguishes it from cirrocumulus which does not show irisations. Ac is seen ahead of older fronts, and large areas of it may be the remains of a once-active front.

When it is lens-shaped it is called Ac lenticularis and is a cloud of the mountains and hills. When it lies in lines with turrets sprouting like battlements out of their tops it is Ac castellanus and this cloud indicates thunder later on many occasions (photo R.2). Accompanying Ac castellanus there is another characteristic pre-thunder

R.2   *Thundery altocumulus. The cloud is arranged in lines with battlements growing out of them (castellanus). In the centre there is some floccus.*

cloud called Ac floccus. This, as its name implies, looks very often like a flock of woolly sheep grazing the blue pastures of the sky (photo C.23). Altostratus (As) is associated with the onset of warm fronts and occlusions. At first it is thin with the sun shining wanly through it (photo C.12). As it thickens the sun disappears and this build-up is very prognostic of coming rain and accompanying wind. It should have been preceded by cirrus and cirrostratus when an active front is in the offing.

Ana fronts   See **Fronts**.

Anemograph   An instrument that draws charts of wind speed and direction. If it should ever be necessary to assess the way the wind varied in some coastal waters, maybe for legal or other purposes, anemograms from representative shore stations are retained in the archives of the various meteorological headquarters but they will need expert evaluation as the exposure and height of the **anemometer** makes profound changes to the winds that blow from seaward.

An actual anemogram for a vicious low that tracked through Valentia on the south-west extremity of Ireland at midnight on 18 October 1984 is given in fig. AR.2. Compare this with the attendant barogram

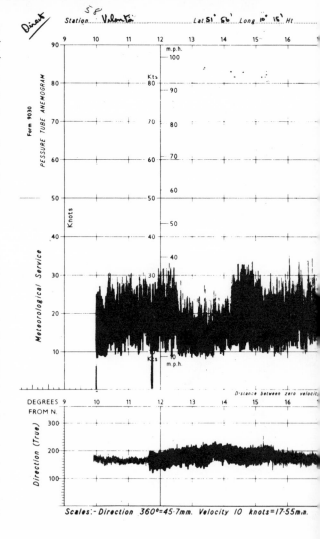

(see **Barograph**). Note that the tops of the gusts experienced were between 60 and 70 kn. (violent storm to hurricane force) but that they did not last long. This kind of low which produces such winds does so very locally and for a relatively short time. If the yacht can survive the onslaught for a while, conditions usually become more manageable within a short period.

Anemometer A device for measuring wind speed. For yachts they may be hand-held or carried at the masthead (photo R.3). The latter are obviously well exposed, but will overestimate the wind speed at sailplan height. Hand-held devices are not well

Fig. AR.2 *An anemogram shows wind speed and direction. It also shows the degree of variability in the wind. In this case whereas the direction was, over most of the time, not very different from the mean, the speed was very variable especially when a frontal trough went through the station.*

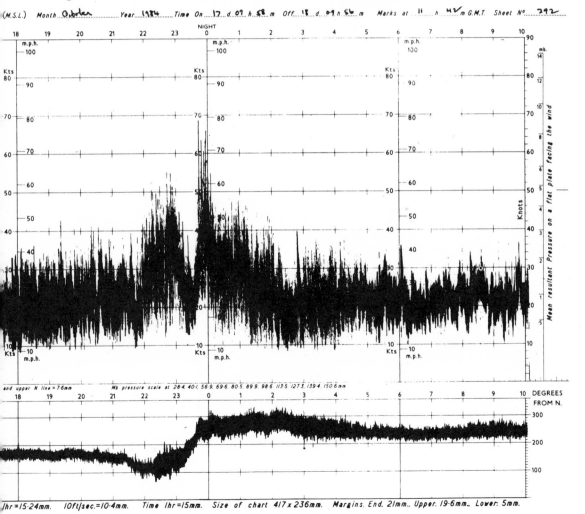

R.3   *A masthead cup anemometer, wind vane and repeater unit of a typical good-quality wind-speed and direction indicator.*

exposed and are easily lost overboard if not secured by a lanyard. They will under-estimate the wind at sailplan height. Both may be the cup variety where three cups are driven round by the wind, but the hand-held types are several, including simple devices like the Ventimeter in which a disc is driven up a central wire by the force of the wind in a plastic transparent tube.

Anticyclones are regions of sinking air and outflowing winds. The air sinks from very high levels and warms as it does so. Thus it evaporates away the higher clouds, but not necessarily the lower ones. Anticyclones can be very cloudy, as fig. AR.3 shows, but the whole trend in anticyclonic conditions is towards rubbing out deep clouds and the rain they produce. Kata fronts are ones where air has sunk over them to such a degree as to have eroded the upper storeys of their clouds. This sinking is called subsidence (pronounced sub-sid-ence) and the air warms adiabatically.

When the subsidence process is well advanced, a temperature inversion is pro-duced relatively near the surface. This subsidence inversion is often impossible to break however hot it may get at the surface. In temperate latitudes when the temperature soars into the 90s and no cloud forms you will have an intense subsidence inversion whose top can be seen at sunset as a definite line of division against the western sky. (See also **Inversions**.) The effect of such inver-sions is to inhibit the wind strength and usually seabreezes are loth to blow.

Anticyclones are either travelling or blocking, and examples of each are to be found in chapters 6 and 7. When long periods of similar weather type invade an area, a blocking high is the cause. When short periods of anticyclonic weather appear, then the high is travelling, usually between lows with changeable conditions.

The typical sequence of wind shifts to expect when a travelling high crosses the sailing area is as follows: NW Force 4–5 decreasing and backing W Force 2–4. Followed later by further backing towards S and increasing Force 4–5 as the next depres-sion follows the high in. (In the SH, for N read S and for W read E.)

The weather chart in fig. AR.3 is chosen

because of its intensely anticyclonic nature. South of 50N pressure is high everywhere from America across the Atlantic and deep into Europe. This is unusual even for summer, but there are useful lessons to be learned from studying the details. Winds blow to keep high pressure on the right (reversed for SH). They are light everywhere except where depressions crowd in. There are calms in the centres of the highs. There is hardly a drop of rain over the whole vast area, but here and there there is mist or fog and occasional drizzle. On the coasts, where the skies are clear, seabreezes have set in.

Trends that do not follow the usual ideas: while great areas are covered in broken cloud or clear skies even vaster domains are covered in cloud. Only over continental landmasses and southern oceans do the expected blue skies appear.

Atmosphere   The shell of air surrounding the Earth (fig. AR.4). Air comprises 78% nitrogen, 21% oxygen plus 1% argon and a variable amount (0.03–0.3%) of carbon

Fig. AR.3   *A chart full of anticyclones. 1200Z 3 July 1969. Pressure is high over North America, the Atlantic, Britain and Europe south of the Baltic. Open circles indicate less than half-cover of cloud.*   *Filled-in circles indicate half-cloudy or more. Note that in the ridge over Britain and the North Sea area generally there are vast areas of cloudiness when textbook ideas say it should be largely cloudless.*

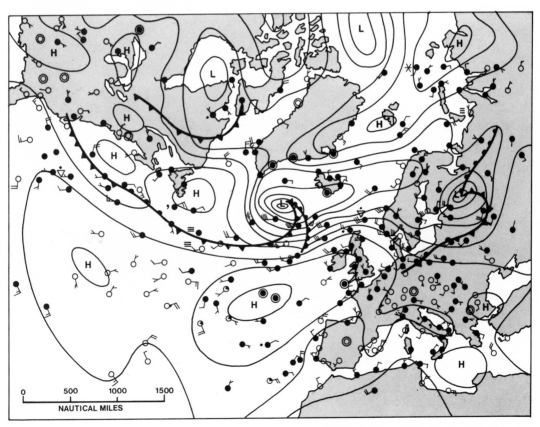

Fig. AR.4   *The major zones of the atmosphere. The sound of explosions and thunder can carry very large distances through being reflected from the warm layer. Thus a 'zone of silence' occurs between where the ground wave of sound dies out and the sky wave comes to earth.*

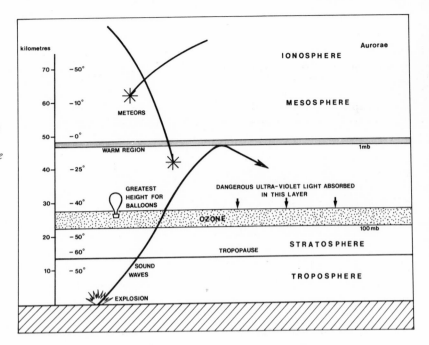

dioxide. There are also traces of hydrogen, neon, helium, krypton and xenon. The other important constituents are water vapour at low levels and ozone (three oxygen atoms in a molecule rather than the two of atmospheric oxygen) in a tenuous shell spanning an altitude of about 25 km (16 miles). Ozone is relatively rare, but manages to absorb all the harmful ultra-violet from the sun that would be damaging to life. Water vapour is relatively abundant and it is the only significant constituent of the atmosphere that absorbs heat radiation from the Earth to space. It thus acts as a heat trap.

Aurora Particles of the solar wind impinging on the very rarefied gases of the upper ionosphere cause the latter to emit light which is the auroral glow. The light is mainly from nitrogen and monatomic oxygen and hence when coloured is predominantly pink or green. Otherwise it is a dawn-like grey-white colour.

Auroral glows can be observed some 600 miles away from the point where they are overhead. The main auroral zones lie between 20° and 25° of either pole and are concentrated there by the effect of the Earth's magnetic field which directs the solar wind away from the equator towards the poles.

The solar wind blows at 'gale force' when sunspot activity is at maximum and then the 'Great Aurora' spreads equatorwards and may in extreme cases be observed in the tropics. The finest displays occur about a day after an intense solar flare has been observed in the central portion of the sun. Then the displays are most highly coloured and can be observed as far as 40°N or S.

During the maximum of the 11-year sunspot cycle, possibly ten displays occur per year along latitudes 50°N or S while 60° sees upwards of 200 nights with aurorae. At the minimum this latter figure can be halved, and 50° sees none at all.

Practical effects associated with intense auroral displays include the displacement by several degrees of compass needles and the fade-out of short-wave radio transmission because the ionospheric reflecting layers are disturbed by the intensity of the solar wind and the effects may last for several days in higher latitudes. In Norway aurorae are known as 'storm lights', and in southern Britain stormy weather has been shown to follow some 10 to 14 days after a brilliant display.

Barograph A self-recording barometer. The pressure sensing element is a pile of aneroid capsules (fig. BR.1). Many 'professional' deep-sea yachtsmen consider a barograph as essential because it shows **barometric tendency** at a glance, and so gives early warning of impending bad weather. For marine use the pen arm must be oil-damped to prevent it leaving the chart in a lively seaway. It is best sited athwartships because slamming will cause irregularities in the trace. Take it home when not in use and put some thin oil on the bearings at regular intervals. Wash the pen in water or methylated spirit whenever the trace grows thick and use only the ink supplied. A stepped trace indicates too much friction between pen and chart. There are bound to be small regular variations in the trace due to pressure increases with gusts and waves and to inertia in the linkage. In any case good exposure to the atmosphere is essential.

The drawn trace is called a barogram, and fig. BR.2 shows one from the Valentia observatory in the extreme south-west corner of Ireland during the passage of a deep and vicious low that tracked through there at midnight, 18 October 1984. See **Anemograph**.

Barometer An instrument for measuring atmospheric pressure. The only practical type for use at sea is the aneroid (literally non-liquid) in which pressure increase or decrease causes the slight compression or expansion of an evacuated capsule. These mechanical movements are transmitted via linkage to a pointer which moves a scale calibrated in either millimetres or inches of mercury or millibars. The principle is the same as shown in fig. BR.1, although an aneroid barometer uses only one or two capsules compared with as many as ten in the barograph.

Barometric correction For practical purposes no corrections need be applied to aneroids when used at sea level. If taken ashore, remember pressure falls roughly by 1 mb for every 30 ft (10 m) of ascent, but except when really taken 300 ft (100 m) or more up it is not worth making corrections. A statement of index error is supplied with good instruments, and any aneroid should be checked with a standard barometer (a met. office will give a check reading over the phone) every so often. (For corrections to standard barometers see Ref. 11.) The 'weather-glass' legends of 'very dry' to

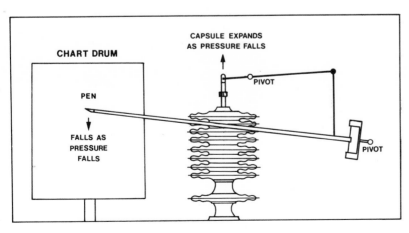

Fig. BR.1 *A simplified diagram of the linkage of an aneroid barograph.*

CAPSULE EXPANDS
AS PRESSURE FALLS

CHART DRUM

PIVOT

PEN

FALLS AS
PRESSURE
FALLS

PIVOT

'stormy' are based on long observation of the type of weather associated with a barometer reading. However, for short-term prognosis only, *tendency* is important. So long as the capsule is not punctured, or the linkage broken or sticking, then the absolute correctness or otherwise of an aneroid barometer is of little consequence because it will still show the all-important tendency to fall or rise and the log should indicate the reading every hour of the watch so that the tendency can be gauged.

Barometric tendency is the change in the barometric pressure with time. The normal practice is to give the change over a three-hour period preceding an observation. Gale-force winds are almost certain to follow a tendency greater than 10 mb/3 h, but considerable variations can occur in the steepness of the barograph trace in three hours and for foretelling gales in the short term the steepening of the tendency is the important thing to watch.

The standard symbols for barometric tendency as used on weather charts are shown in fig. BR.3. It is assumed that the observations of the barogram are made every three hours on the hour. Note that the barometer could have fallen temporarily when the tendency symbol is apparently showing a continuous rise, and similarly it can rise for a time even when the symbol indicates a fall.

Obviously the barometer does not have to fall at a rate of 10 mb/3 h for a whole

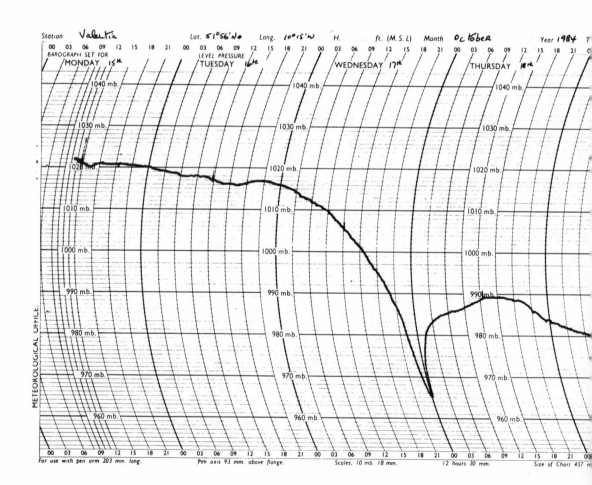

three hours to indicate gale, and whenever the 'slope' of the barogram exceeds the above rate, gale should be expected. Vicious localised storm centres have barograms akin to fig. BR.4. At the sides slopes of 10 mb/3 h and 20 mb/3 h are shown. On the right are corresponding rises. On transferring these slopes to touch the barogram we see that at 'A' Force 8 gale would be expected, and as the slope of the barogram steepens towards the trough at B, then the slope approaches 20 mb/3 h and storm force 10 should be allowed for. The wind will often suddenly shift *cyclonically* on passage of the 'eye' of the disturbance and blow as strongly if not more strongly as the barometer shoots up (C) for rapid rise is just as prognostic of imminent wind as

rapid fall. The wind can still be gale beyond D, but will begin to abate as the barogram flattens out. This barogram is not meant to represent any specific situation.

Beaufort letters are used to record the state of present and past weather in the log and wherever a shorthand notation is required. Capital letters mean intense or heavy, suffix o means slight, prefix i means intermittent, p means passing shower of, and the repeat of a letter indicates continuous. Past weather is indicated by a solidus thus: p/rr = shower now after continuous moderate rain in the last hour. bc/iR = fair now after intermittent heavy rain in last hour. (See table on page 139.)

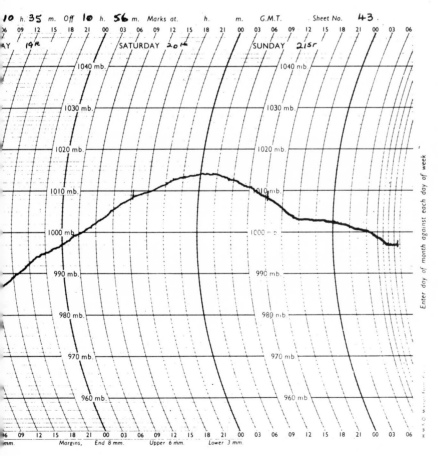

Fig. BR.2   *The barogram for the week which included the day of fig. AR.2. The 975 mb bottom of the pressure trace coincided with the 70 kn. gusts. The reader should compare this with the similar barograms of survival storms in Ref. 7.*

Fig. BR.3 *A barogram for 18 hours showing how the trace would be interpreted in the international code at the end of each three-hour period. Not every fluctuation in the trace can be described.*

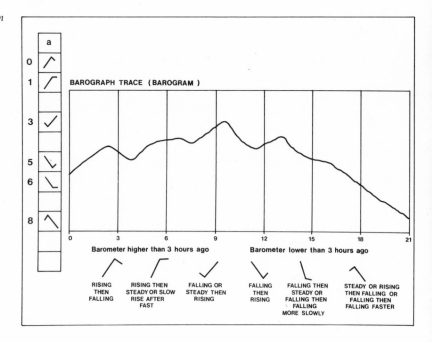

Fig. BR.4 *The slope of the barogram indicates the imminent wind force to be expected.*

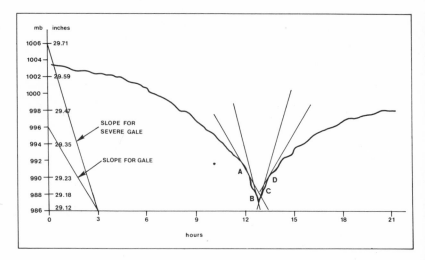

Beaufort letter		*Plotting symbol*
r	rain	●
d	drizzle	,
s	snow	✱
p	shower	▽
h	hail	△
th	thunderstorm	ꓘ
q	squall	∀
m	mist	═
f	fog	≡
z	haze	∞
b	bright or sunny	◔
bc	fair	◑
c	cloudy }	●
o	overcast }	●
x	sky obscured	⊗

Beaufort scale of wind force See pages 140 to 142.

Because gustiness is as hazardous as more sustained wind, in Britain the following criteria are used:

Gusts expected to reach	
43 or more knots	Gale Force 8
52 or more	Severe gale Force 9
61 or more	Storm Force 10
69 or more	Violent storm Force 11
78 or more	Hurricane Force 12

Forecasters also take into account the expected mean wind speeds so that gales are not forecast on isolated or infrequent strong gusts. Note that the term 'hurricane' or 'hurricane force' as used here does not signify that the winds are due to a tropical revolving storm.

Bora is the large-scale mountain wind in the Adriatic which stems from the Dolomites and the Dinaric Alps. It usually comes behind a cold front when the gradient is for winds from over the mountains. It can be a dangerous wind rising from 15 to over 50 kn. sometimes and at times when one would not expect the wind to increase, such as evening time. Bora gales on the Yugoslavian coast last an average 12 hours, and strong bora can last for 40 hours and occasionally days.

Boundary layer When thinking of skin friction of a yacht's hull we imagine the thin layer closest to the hull where the speed increases from that of the surrounding still water to that of the hull. A similar idea applies on a much grander scale to the atmosphere and in the reverse sense. The atmospheric boundary layer is on average about 2000 ft deep and it is where the turbulence induced by surface obstacles and by convection currents is always trying to mix the air. The so-called mixing layer deepens when the wind speed increases and can become zero thickness in calm conditions (e.g. at night over land). It is an important concept to the sailor as it is from the top of the mixing layer that the highest speed gusts come. This is because when the air is normally mixed the wind speed increases with height, but the turbulent eddies and sinking convection currents bring the higher-speed wind on to the surface in gusts (fig. BR.5).

Beaufort scale of wind force

Symbol	Beaufort number	General description	Limit of mean speed (knots)	Land signs
◎	0	Calm	Less than 1	Smoke rises vertically. Leaves do not stir
	1	Light air	1–3	Smoke drifts. Wind vanes do not respond
	2	Light breeze	4–6	Wind felt on the face. Leaves rustle. Light flags not extended. Wind vanes respond
	3	Gentle breeze	7–10	Light flags extended. Leaves in constant motion
	4	Moderate breeze	11–16	Most flags extend fully. Small branches move. Dust and loose paper may be raised
	5	Fresh breeze	17–21	Small trees in leaf sway. Tops of tall trees in noticeable motion
	6	Strong breeze	22–27	Large branches in motion. Whistling heard in wires
	7	Near gale (American usage: Moderate gale)	28–33	Whole trees in motion. Inconvenience felt when walking against wind
	8	Gale (Fresh gale)	34–40	Twigs broken off trees. Generally impeded progress on foot. Rarely experienced inland
	9	Strong gale (Strong gale)	41–47	Chimney pots and slates removed. Fences blown down, etc.

Deep keel criteria	State of sea	Symbols used on charts
Boom swings idly in the swell. Racing flags and anemometers will not respond. Flies and tell tails might just	Sea mirror-smooth. Calm enough to preserve shape of reflections of sails, masts, etc.	Calm
Sails just fill, but little way made. Racing flags and vanes may respond but cup anemometers may not. Flies and tell tails respond. Spinnakers do not fill	Scaly or shell-shaped ripples. No foam crests to be seen on open sea	1–2 kt.
Wind felt on the cheek. Controlled way made. Spinnakers and sails generally fill. Racing flags and anemometers respond and are reliable	Small short wavelets with glassy crests that do not break	3–7
Good way made. Light flags fully extended	Large wavelets. Crests may break but foam is of glassy appearance. A few scattered white horses may be seen when wind at upper limit	8–12
Best general working breeze for all craft. Genoas at optimum	Small waves lengthen. Fairly frequent white horses	13–17
Craft's way somewhat impeded by seaway. Genoas near their limit. Spinnakers still carried. Yachts approach maximum speed	Moderate waves. Many white horses	18–22
Edge of 'yacht gale' force. Cruising craft seek shelter. Reefing recommended to meet gusts when cruising	Large waves form and extensive foam crests are prevalent. Spray may be blown off some wave tops	23–27
Yacht gale force when most cruising craft seek shelter. Racing yachts may just carry spinnakers. Reefing essential	Sea heaps up and white foam from breaking waves begins to be blown in streaks along the wind direction	28–32
Gale force in anybody's language. Only necessity or ocean racing keeps craft at sea. Set storm canvas or heave-to	Moderately high waves of greater length. Edges of crests begin to break into spindrift. Foam blown in well-marked streaks along the wind	33–37
Unless ocean racing – and sometimes even then – craft seek deep water. Run towing warps, etc. This may be survival force for most	High waves. Dense streaks of foam along the wind. Crests begin to topple, tumble and roll over	38–42
		43–47

continued

Beaufort scale of wind force

Symbol	Beaufort number	General description	Limit of mean speed (knots)	Land signs
⟨symbol⟩	10	Storm (Whole gale)	48–55	Very rare inland. Trees uprooted; considerable structural damage
	11	Violent storm	56–63	
	12	Hurricane force	64 and over	

In the tropics, where the well-known balance between pressure gradient force and geostrophic force weakens, boundary layer analyses and prognoses such as fig. 21.2 (from the fax station at Norfolk, Va) become important to the mariner to tell him what the surface wind field actually is. This kind of chart uses streamlines and so they appear where air is sinking on to the surface and disappear where it is rising off the surface. On the whole the surface winds follow the streamlines because this is the winter. In summer they are much less likely to, and even on this chart we see various oddities probably produced by local variations in water temperature. Over Yucatan we see a convergence zone with winds blowing in from east and west and winds blowing out north and south. Such things are possible with streamlines, but not with isobars. Local small-scale storm areas can produce winds such as at 60W, 15N much in excess of the general run. The dotted lines are isotachs – lines of equal wind speed – and these can be useful to the mariner as indicating the level of wind speed he can expect.

However, the weather of the tropics can be difficult to forecast as the weather is vastly more under the control of thermal than of pressure forces. See also chapter 21 and **Gradient wind**.

Buys Ballot's law   First formulated by Professor Buys Ballot of Utrecht in 1857.

(NH) Stand *back* to the wind and pressure is *low* on the *left*.

(SH) Stand *facing* the wind and pressure is *low* on the *left*.

This rule only applies to the middle latitudes. Local winds such as sea and land breezes, mountain and valley wind, etc. do not obey the law.

Castellated clouds   See **Alto clouds**.

Centigrade (Celsius) scale is that scale of temperature which marks 0° at the temperature of equilibrium between water and ice

Deep keel criteria	State of sea	Symbols used on charts	
Almost the ultimate for yachts. Only chance in deep water and with sea room to run before it or possibly lie to a sea anchor	Very high waves with long overhanging crests. The whole surface of the sea takes on a white appearance. Tumbling of sea heavy and shocklike. Visibility impaired		48–52
	Exceptionally high waves. The sea is completely covered with long white patches of foam lying along the direction of the wind. Everywhere edges of wave crests are blown into froth. Visibility impaired		53–57
	The air is filled with foam and spray. Sea completely white with driving spray; visibility very seriously impaired		58–72

Note that the wind arrows as used internationally on charts do not fit the convention for Beaufort force given on the extreme left. In Beaufort, one fleche = 2 forces while in the international notation one fleche = 10 kn. (± 2 kn.).

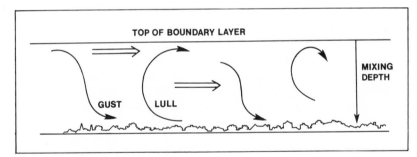

Fig. BR.5   *Turbulent overturnings in the lowest layer reach up so high and no higher. This depth is called the mixing depth. It has a profound effect on sailing.*

(ice point) and 100° at the temperature of equilibrium between water and steam under standard atmospheric pressure (steam point). The fundamental interval between is divided into 100 grades or degrees hence the name, and under the name Celsius it is used as a domestic scale in many countries of the world. On the right are the rough sensation values of temperatures on the Celsius scale.

0°C and all minus values	Freezing
5°C	Cold
10°C	Chilly
15°C	Mild
20°C	Warm
25°C	Hot
30°C	Very hot

Below is a conversion scale.

Climate is the average weather conditions in any locality and is governed by three factors: latitude, position relative to continents and oceans, and local geographic conditions. Continental climate is experienced in the interiors and in the eastern parts of the great continents. Here rainfall is small and humidity low, and there is a maximum range of temperature both between day and night and between summer and winter. Western parts of the continents and islands have an oceanic climate where rainfall is heavier and humidity higher, and temperature tends to remain at a more uniform level because of close proximity to the sea.

Temperature and rainfall are the most important factors in climate, but only near the equator are yearly mean temperatures representative. Elsewhere monthly means are more helpful, and these are the average of the daily means. The latter are the average of the maximum and minimum temperatures recorded each day.

Sea temperatures control the air temperatures over the oceans, but the winds must first have a long fetch. In the lee of east coasts the climate is representative of the land areas rather than the sea, whereas on west coasts oceanic climates prevail.

Over the oceans winds and current circulations tend to parallel one another and sea surface isotherms follow suit.

Cloud is composed of water droplets, snowflakes or ice crystals or mixtures of all three. Any process that lifts air can lead to the formation of cloud. Thus the major methods of formation include:

(a) warm air being lifted up over cold air as happens at warm and cold fronts. Such lifting leads to extensive layer clouds.

(b) cool air flowing over a warmer surface which leads to heap clouds and possibly showers.

(c) turbulent eddies which lift surface air sufficiently high to produce low-level billow clouds that often cover the whole sky.

(d) interference between two layers of air moving at different speeds. Wave motion is produced at the interface between the two layers and forms of Sc, Ac and Cc result which have the appearance of waves on the seashore.

(e) air lifted over hills and mountains (orographic cloud). Such action can induce extensive cloudiness on the windward slopes and over the tops in conditions when elsewhere it is largely cloudless.

(f) waves in an airstream over and downwind of hill ridges and mountain ranges. Such waves produce lens-shaped clouds (Sc or Ac or Cc lenticularis) that may remain stationary or suddenly disappear to reappear elsewhere (photo R.4).

(g) convergence of air such as occurs along seabreeze fronts. In effect surface winds collide and the only way of escape for the air is upwards. This leads to lines of heap clouds which, in certain circumstances, may be the only clouds in the sky.

Clouds are classified: (i) by height – there are three height decks: low, medium and high; (ii) by shape – there are two distinct shapes: layer and heap (fig. CR.1). The names of medium and high clouds follow a logical pattern, but low clouds have special names not necessarily fitting the following scheme:

Medium level clouds are prefixed 'alto'
High level clouds are prefixed 'cirro'
Heap clouds are called cumulus or related names
Layer clouds are called stratus or related names

Thus we have altocumulus (Ac) and altostratus (As) as the two basic cloud types found in the medium levels of the troposphere. The high clouds are cirrocumulus

R.4 *Strato-cumulus lenticularis formed by wave streaming over the mountains of Wales. Wave clouds like this often indicate coming frontal weather.*

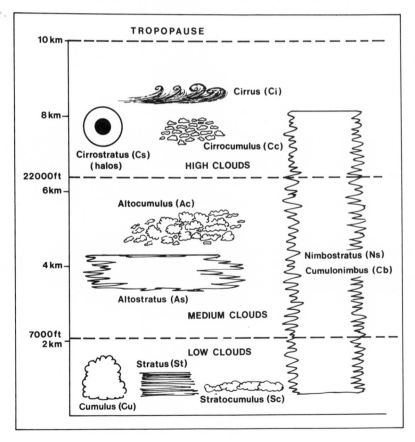

Fig. CR.1 *The simple classification of clouds is all that the average mariner will need to identify the major types that mean something weatherwise.*

(Cc) and cirrostratus (Cs), but include a third special form, cirrus (Ci). Low clouds may be stratus (St) when formed in a layer, cumulus (Cu) when in heaps, and strato-cumulus (Sc) when formed in a layer of heaps. As well as these we have the two rain-bearing cloud types, nimbostratus (Ns) and cumulonimbus (Cb), both of which span the height decks. The word 'nimbus' means rain-bearing. As these basic types do not cover all the forms, further descriptive suffixes may be added. For example, the scud of bad weather is stratus fractus (St frac) and the chaotic skies that precede thunder include altocumulus castellanus (As cast) and altocumulus floccus (Ac floc). The deep half-way stage between cumulus and cumulonimbus is described by cumulus congestus (Cu con) – photo C.17. Most of the important variants are described under the respective headings throughout the book.

Cloud height is for the non-specialist a very difficult thing to judge. However, from the practical point of view exact height is unimportant: only relative height matters. Height can be judged from form and colour. Totally white clouds without shadowing are made of ice crystals and so must be high up. The elements will look small by distance and the characteristic fall streaks of Ci, or the haloes in Cs, give away the height. Small Ac need only be differentiated from Cc by the professional observer. The difference is immaterial in the case of the individual weather forecaster as they both mean the same thing: instability and wind shear at height that accompany changeable weather. Medium-level clouds show shadows in their thicker parts and can often be seen to be below cirrus clouds or contrails. Sometimes the shadow of a trail lies like a dark lane across thin Ac or As, showing the latter to be lower. Low clouds like cumulus are obviously low, and medium-level cloud islands are obviously above them. When St closes in, then the base is often so amorphous that it is impossible to assess its height. Just say a few hundred feet or less and you are often right.

When bad weather approaches, As forms and lowers, but the space below it remains for a while cloud-free. Then cloud layers form there and they are due to falling rain evaporating and wetting-up the space. The rain may not reach the ground. This cloud is St pannus, and it will extend to eventually become a total cover that obscures the true cloudbase which is lost above it. Pannus is the stratus that precedes the front and accompanies it. Fractus is the stratus that hangs wisp-like below the passing frontal cloud outlined against the coming clearance.

Cloud cover is for most purposes sufficiently measured in quarters of the sky covered. Less than a quarter covered may be described as sunny by day or clear by night or as blue sky by day. A quarter to three-quarters covered will be described as fair so long as no precipitation or fog exists, and more than three-quarters covered is described as cloudy. Overcast means that a solid uniform layer exists across the whole sky. The cloud cover is more intense than when described as cloudy. Sky obscured is used when fog is so dense that the sky cannot be seen and therefore it is not known how much is covered with cloud. On professional weather maps the cloud cover is given in octas or eighths of the dome of the sky covered. The merest trace of cloud will be registered as ⅛ and clear sky really means absolutely no cloud. The symbols within station circles are as follows:

Code figure	N			
0	○	5	◒	
1	◔	6	◑	
2	◕	7	◕	9 = sky obscured
3	◕	8	●	/ = sky not observed
4	◑	9	⊗	
		/	⊠	

Cloudiness tends to go with the continuation (for a while at least) of the existing conditions. The 8/8 low cloud associated with frontal rain-belts keeps the same wind conditions under it until it clears. When the sky opens, so, often, does the wind change with it, either shifting direction or speed or both. A low level of variation in the look of the sky goes with a similar low level of variation in the microstructure of the wind. Big cumulus and cumulonimbus clouds bring big gusts and corresponding lulls in the wind.

Cloudiness damps out the diurnal changes in temperature and so wind speed. It prevents radiation from the earth that leads to fog and frost. However, if cloud appears over a fog layer, then the latter is with you for quite a time. On most coasts one or other of the wind directions is associated with cloudiness. In Atlantic Europe it is the SW wind and on the east coast of North America it is the SE wind.

The coastline is often a division between cloud and no cloud. In photo 23.1 we note how lines of smaller cumulus (cloud streets) have formed across the land masses in the direction of the wind. Ireland and the west coasts of England and Wales are islands of cloud edged by clear skies over the sea. The same goes for France and the Low Countries. The contrast in temperature between land and sea in spring leads to much convective cloud over land when little will appear over the sea. In autumn it is the opposite.

The sea fog in photo R.9 shuns the land and sticks to the sea. It is 'burned off' as soon as it tries to invade the land.

Cold front   Where a relatively warm airmass is replaced by a cool or cold airmass a cold front exists. The cold front is structurally a warm front in reverse, and as most warm and cold fronts form from waves in the polar front it is evident that only the different way they move gives them their own separate characteristics (fig. CR.2). For example, many cold fronts are accompanied in their onset by intense showery-type precipitation and by sudden and sometimes violent squalls. There is often a much greater veer of wind across the surface cold front (SCF) than occurs at the surface warm front (SWF).

The first signs of a cold front are usually an ominous-looking line squall coming in from the right of windward with odd contrary cloud motions showing considerable turbulent mixing. This is caused by the cold air driving in under the warm air and setting it off into showers and sometimes

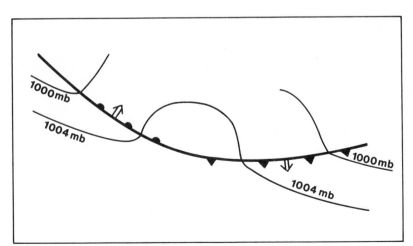

Fig. CR.2   *When the cold front of one depression becomes the warm front of the next, there is a weak ridge between. However, they are still the same front – just moving in opposite directions.*

thunderstorms. Thunder in winter is almost always due to the passage of a vigorous cold front. The heavy rain band does not last long and is replaced by more continuous rain. Again, as described with the warm front, this so-called continuous rain is heavier in bands, and tails away to lighter rain between and behind the bands.

The cold front rain passes in about half the time it took the warm front rain to pass, and then the back edge of the front is visible as a more or less straight edge with cirrus clouds pushing fallstreaks down towards the retreating warm airmass. It is characteristic to have pencil-thin skeins of cloud (one or two in number) stretched along and parallel to the back edge of the clearing cold-front cloud. The motion of the cirrus immediately behind a cold-front clearance is important as it tells you whether a new depression is in the offing or whether a ridge or a high is building to the west. If the crossed winds orientation for colder air is well in evidence, e.g. surface wind from NW and cirrus moving from SW, expect showers at first but further outlook anticyclonic.

A modern view of the structure of an ana-cold front is shown in fig. CR.3

(Ref. 5). It has been measured that the updraught in the Cb clouds forming the line squall at the leading edge is between 15 and 20 times the vertical rate of ascent in the cloud wedge following. Just as with the warm front there will often be convective cells (mesoscale precipitation areas or MPAs) within and sticking out of the top of the cloud wedge. You can look out for these when jetting to foreign climes or maybe on internal flights.

It is obviously the line squall at the leading edge of the ana-cold front that is most important for yachts, as while it lasts it can be vicious. It is useful to ascertain roughly when any incipient cold front is likely to cross your area (see page 65). For hints on the action to be taken when threatened by a cold front see page 64.

There are kata-cold fronts as there are kata-warm fronts where subsidence has eroded much of the upper cloud and only some banks of As, Ac and Sc still exist. The surface weather is cloudy, but the rainfall is light and may appear almost like drizzle.

Comma clouds are the characteristic shape of active depressions as seen from space. The TIROS N photo (R.5) of the low

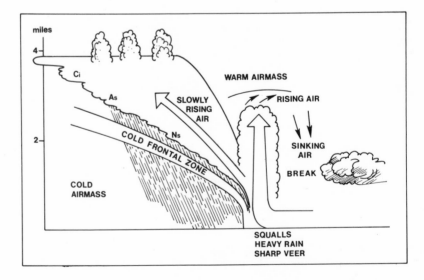

Fig. CR.3 *The structure of an ana-cold front showing where the squall line is. The diagram is after Browning and Harrold (Ref. 5).*

miles

4—

Ci

As

WARM AIRMASS

SLOWLY RISING AIR

RISING AIR

COLD FRONTAL ZONE

Ns

2—

SINKING AIR

BREAK

COLD AIRMASS

SQUALLS
HEAVY RAIN
SHARP VEER

R.5   *A comma cloud which hides a yachting disaster. The depression which devastated the Fastnet fleet in 1979 imaged on the afternoon of 13 August by TIROS-N in the visible.*

which devastated the Fastnet fleet over the night of 13/14 August 1979 shows just what is meant by the term 'comma'. The modern theory of conveyor belts (see **Depressions**) explains the way the cloud shield and the trailing fronts assume the shape of a giant comma. The satellite was overhead at 1537Z on 13 August 1979: this is a visible wavelength picture.

Conduction is the transfer of heat through from places of higher to those of lower temperature. Solids conduct heat in much the same way as they conduct electricity.

R.6 *Cumulo-nimbus. Looking east along this beach the shower cloud is moving on westerly winds. The horizon is obscured by falling rain (bottom left) while outriding smaller cumuli occupy the edges of the cloud's personal space. Overhead descending currents behind the shower induce characteristic clouds that are very close to being mamma.*

Metals conduct heat well, and insulators such as plastics conduct it badly. Compacted granular materials conduct heat better than loose ones do because the latter are more full of air cavities, and air (or any other gas) is a very poor conductor of heat. If you have a substance like glass wool or similar it is really a web of air cavities, and as they are small so convection is inhibited too so that heat is retained or kept out depending on the requirements. You can see this on a just frosty morning when any freshly dug earth is covered in frost whereas the surrounding undisturbed soil is frost free. What has happened is that the earth's stored heat has not managed to conduct upwards through the air cavities of the loose soil, but has been able to do so through the undisturbed ground.

The ability of the earth or the sea to absorb heat in depth and give it back slowly through the autumn and winter is the major factor in the amelioration of climate. All oceanic places will have mild climates compared with continental ones. Coasts facing the prevailing wind will be warmer than those that face other directions.

Convergence occurs when more air enters an air column over any place than leaves it. Pressure rises at the surface. See **Pressure**. However, convergent surface winds lead to calms and fitful winds as with seabreeze fronts as well as inducing convective storms when conditions favour them.

Coriolis force is the apparent force on any fluid in motion on the Earth which tends to deflect it to one side or the other of its path. The **geostrophic** force is a form of Coriolis force which is particularly applied to air motion. When the effect refers to ocean currents, the Coriolis force is used to explain why they rotate right-handed (NH) and left-handed (SH). See also **Gradient wind**.

Corona   See **Haloes**.

Crepuscular rays are the phenomenon associated with the saying 'the sun is drawing water'. Needless to say the sun does not draw water by this or any other method, but the rays are shafts of sunlight coming through chinks in the clouds into a dusty or smoky atmosphere below. Their

C.13   (above) With less organised fronts than the pictures
C.11 and C.12 indicate you can get irisations in the
gathering banks of altostratus, but although you should not
ignore their message they may not mean very strong wind
to come.

C.14   (below) The rain-bearing cloud is nimbostratus with
the form of stratus called pannus developing below it. When
the pannus spreads across the whole sky it will drop the
cloudbase to near the deck sometimes.

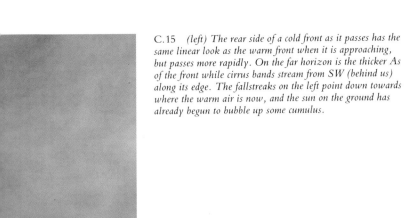

C.15 *(left) The rear side of a cold front as it passes has the same linear look as the warm front when it is approaching, but passes more rapidly. On the far horizon is the thicker As of the front while cirrus bands stream from SW (behind us) along its edge. The fallstreaks on the left point down towards where the warm air is now, and the sun on the ground has already begun to bubble up some cumulus.*

C.16 *(below) Sea fog is variable. Here the sun on the cliffs has cleared a strip along the coast. We see how shallow the fog is, but that is still deeper than any yacht caught in it. Over the sea such fog cannot be cleared by the sun as would happen over land.*

C.17 (above) Cumulus that may or may not get big
enough to develop into showers. You have to keep an eye on
this development because the afternoon could be quite squally.

C.18 (below) A thundery trough approaches. Do not be
fooled by the fact that there are, as yet, no anvils. The
cloud development on the right shows a cumulonimbus in
the hail stage.

C.19 *(right) The characteristic trademark of the big shower or thunderstorm is the anvil top. You are looking at the tropopause when you see the false cirrus spread out like this. This is an old storm cell. The real trouble may be in the lesser surrounding clouds as they grow.*

C.20 *(below) The strange bulbous form of mamma – so called because it resembles a cow's udders. Mamma appears both ahead of and (as here) behind big storm cells. If you see mamma in coming thunder clouds, allow for the possibility of tornadoes over land. They are rare over the coasts.*

C.21 (left) The loss of the horizon in the centre shows that the rather innocuous-looking cloud above is producing quite a moderate shower. Heavier showers will blot out marks, but not for long.

C.22 (below) The battlements on these lines of altocumulus cloud give them the name of castellanus. They indicate that the medium layers are unstable and so later a much deeper layer may be unstable enough for thunderstorms. Often the storms break out over the surface of a front.

C.23 (above) The woolly sheep-like look of this alto cloud gives it its name of *floccus*. Together with *castellanus* this cloud says look out for thunder later. Use the crossed-winds rules on its motion to see if deterioration is indicated.

C.24 (below) Later than C.22 and C.23 the thundery cloud increases. The visibility is often poor (as here) when these thundery outbreaks are building up.

R.7 *Cumulus. These examples are slightly larger than true fair-weather Cu, but still may not grow into showers. They have the characteristic flat bases and rounded tops of such clouds.*

prognostic value is limited. They reveal a broken sky and below it a stable airmass, both of which indicate stability and so a continuation of fair weather for a while at least.

Cumulonimbus (Cb) is the name given to big cumulus clouds that produce showers and to thunderstorm clouds. Such clouds are of great vertical development and often the upper parts spread out in an anvil of false cirrus. The base often resembles Ns and is about 1 km (3000 ft) up, but fracto-stratus (scud) forms below the true base in the heavy rain and hail that occurs (photo R.6).

The nature of Cb changes with the wind speed. With gale-force winds showers are very ragged and only along cold fronts can a storm cell grow to produce an isolated clap of thunder. Such claps are associated with severe cyclonic weather.

With wind speeds of Force 4–5, large and frequent showers can grow in the airstream when the latter is mP or a similar airmass, and over land they are typical of spring when surface temperatures are rising but air temperatures are still relatively low.

Thunderstorms can develop deeply when the airstream is relatively slow moving (about 20 kn. in the middle layers) and can then extend to the tropopause over wide areas. See **Thunderstorms**.

Cumulus (Cu) clouds are rounded indi-idual clouds with dome-shaped tops and flat bases, normally associated with fair weather (photo R.7). They are the clouds that give the 'silver-lining' effect on the sunset horizon. True Cu tends to be flattened on the top as it grows in an airstream which is only unstable in the surface deck in which it develops. There are many intermediate forms between true Cu and developed Cb and the day's heating over land can mean Cu in the morning and Cb in the afternoon. A criterion for possible showers is when individual elements grow deeper than the distance ground to base. The trunks of such clouds should be solid and not spindly like chimneys. In the latter case no showers can result. Cumulus is the cloud of the oceans because statistically the air temperature is about a degree higher than the underlying sea surface throughout much of the world.

Cyclone is a term that has several meanings. Strictly any vortex whose winds rotate anticlockwise (NH) or clockwise (SH) is a cyclone. In practice there are extra tropical cyclones (depressions or lows) and tropical cyclones (hurricanes, etc.). It is the latter to which the name cyclone is usually applied.

Cyclones differ from lows fundamentally in that in the cyclone the winds rotate the same way at all levels whereas the low is moderated and controlled by having a different path for the winds at height than nearer the surface. (See **Tropical revolving storms**.)

Cyclonic is a word used in two major senses. The word is used in shipping forecasts when a low is going to track through a sea area and the wind-shifts are impossible to describe. Then the mariner is expected to use his own ideas of how winds will shift when a low tracks through to the south or north of him or possibly comes straight across him.

Whenever isobars curve in the sense of enclosing lower pressure, they are said to be cyclonically curved (fig. CR.4). Cyclonic curvature goes with ascending air and so with cloud and precipitation. Thus the weather is worse under cyclonically curved isobars. Typical cyclonic changes are as follows:

(1)   Yacht A making westward passage may have SW Force 6 on the leading periphery of this low. Yacht B in the path of the centre Force 5 from S or SE and yacht C on the north side could have a light easterly.

(2)   As the centre passes, A's wind must veer to say SW while B will experience the lightening and backing close to the calm eye where the winds change over to become, say, light to moderate NW after a light variable period. Yacht C must expect a backing wind without much increase.

(3)   In the rear of the retreating low, A has shifted on to starboard tack as the wind has gone on veering. Yacht B will experience a wind that picks up more purposefully from say NW while yacht C may well find an increase as

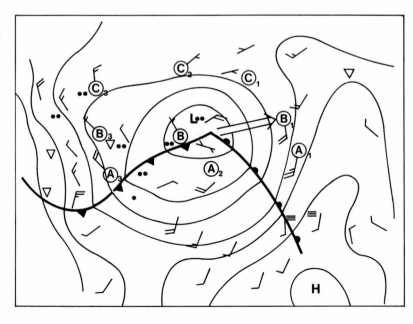

Fig. CR.4   *When faced with the shipping forecast word 'cyclonic', the mariner has to recognise from wind direction, etc. where the centre is likely to track. This diagram should help.*

the wind backs round through north. These are typical cyclonic changes in NH. There will be corresponding changes in SH.

Deepening refers to a low whose central pressure is falling with time. A low that deepens rapidly induces gales in its circulation as pressure in surrounding areas will not fall at the same rate and the gradient must tighten. Occasionally and normally only in the winter certain depressions deepen 'explosively', i.e. at such a rapid rate as to make it inevitable that storm-force winds will result. (See **Gales** and **Barometric tendency**.)

Density is the mass of a unit volume of a substance. For example a cubic metre of dry air has a mass of about 1 kg, and a cubic metre of water has a mass of 1000 kg, so water is a thousand times denser than air. Objects that float will have a density less than that of water. Relative density or specific gravity is a number that expresses how dense a substance is compared with water. Density decreases with temperature increase for all fluids except water which has its maximum density at 4°C. Water is strange in that its solid form (ice) is less dense than its liquid form. Thus icebergs float and so does all ice however it is formed. Young arctic icebergs have about five-sixths of their mass under water which decreases to a half for much-weathered icebergs. Some icebergs called 'growlers' are very dangerous as they are only just awash.

The density of sea water is higher than that of fresh water because of its salinity. Open sea water freezes at −2°C (28.6°F), but fresh-water seas such as the Baltic freeze at just below freezing point (31.5°F).

Depressions are the cyclones of the temperate latitudes. Most, but not all, start off as kinks in the polar front which forms as in fig. DR.1a when a cold airmass (mP) comes into juxtaposition with a warm one

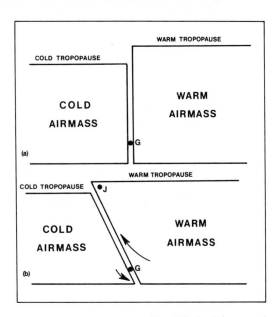

Fig. DR.1 *Theory and practice show that when two airmasses come together the zone of division between them must develop a slope. This is a frontal surface in the process of formation.*

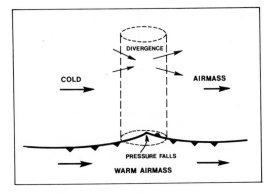

Fig. DR.2 *It is divergence at some altitude that allows the surface pressure to fall when a depression is born as a wave in the polar front.*

(mT). The vertical zone of division soon becomes a slope with the cold air under-cutting the warm and the warm air lying over the cold (fig. DR.1b). The jetstream J occupies a position just below the break in the tropopause and within the warm air. The loss of potential energy as the centre of gravity G of the total mass falls with time is transformed into the kinetic energy of the winds. The fact that the end product of the depression's life-cycle is the transport of lighter warm air aloft to be replaced by denser cooler air at the surface shows that this is indeed the case.

Looked at from the surface division between the airmasses (fig. DR.2) surface pressure falls at the tip of the kink or wave in the polar front. This is due to complex developments that lead to more air flowing out of the air column over the wave than is flowing into it. This **divergence** lowers the total mass of air and so the weight of the column is reduced and pressure falls.

Dynamic considerations will eventually lead to a full-blown depression with a warm sector and overlain by a cloud shield (fig. DR.3). This can occur when sufficient length of front exists for the low to get elbow-room to develop. Something over a thousand miles of undisturbed front is required to allow the full development. Otherwise the wave depression whips along the front at high speed and eventually dies out, having temporarily deteriorated the weather in its vicinity as it goes (fig. 23.1).

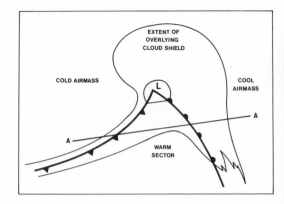

Fig. DR.3   *The shape of the cloud shield over the depression in its prime and the way cloud invades the warm sector need new explanations of upper-air motions as shown in fig. DR.5.*

A vertical cross-section along the line A–A (fig. DR.4) shows how the warm frontal zone is a layer separating cool air below from relatively warm air above it. However, as Ci and Cs are ice-crystal clouds, this shows that the air is only warm by contrast. We see the important cloud sequence that foretells coming trouble: cirrus, followed by cirrostratus (haloes about sun and moon) which thickens into altostratus (As) and eventually (when it rains or snows) nimbostratus (Ns). Pannus is a form of stratus that forms in the wet air under the cloudbase of the Ns and lowers the base to perhaps a thousand feet or so. It

Fig. DR.4 *A modern view of the cross-section through the fronts of the depression shown in fig. DR.3 has to include reasons for rain appearing in the warm sector.*

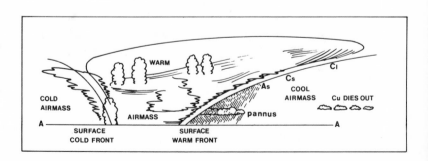

may over the sea be lower than this in bad weather conditions.

The warm air finally gives way to cold air again when the cold front has passed, but not before some often vicious weather has had to be met. The big cumulonimbus clouds shown at altitude in the warm air are mesoscale precipitaton areas (MPAs) which lead to variations in the surface rainfall and also allow for rain occurring in the warm sector.

Older theories of the air motions in depressions have proved to be only part of the truth, and radar and aircraft studies of the airflows have shown that, as in fig. DR.5, the depression draws air from the high-pressure regions to the south and south-east of it and feeds it up two great conveyor belts (Ref. 6). The cold conveyor transports relatively cold air gently upwards along and over the space ahead of the warm front, i.e. up through the cloud wedge of

the warm front. It then turns to combine its winds with the warm conveyor that has brought warmer air up over the warm sector. At cirrus levels the two conveyors transport moist stable air down from between NW and W at altitude just as we described in chapter 4 when discussing the crossed-winds rules.

The envelope of these gently ascending air currents forms the shape of the cloud shield over the depression that is observed on the satellite pictures and which has spawned the name **comma clouds** because of their shape (see photo R.5). Further, in these ascending conveyors MPAs are generated so that rain occurs ahead of cold fronts where, on the older theories, it should not be able to do so. The steady rainfall associated with warm fronts is also added to and made variable by the more intense local falls from these high-level clouds that are quite invisible from the ground.

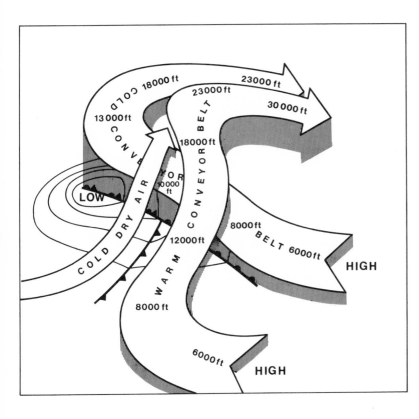

Fig. DR.5 *How the conveyor belt model explains how air lifting over the warm sector can set off rain there; why the upper winds come in from around W to NW well ahead of the depression; why the cloud shield has the shape it has. (After Carlson, Ref. 6.)*

In addition, behind the cold front a cold dry conveyor sweeps in along the back edge of the cold-front cloud. Again this comes from SW, which is the direction we emphasised was the one to be looked for in association with NW gradient winds as the depression passed. These conveyors are only fully established when a depression has become mature, but they remain important features after the occlusion process has set in. The way the lows grow on the equatorial side of the jet streams and their subsequent motion with respect to it have been covered in chapter 5.

Dewpoint is the temperature to which air must be cooled so that the water vapour it contains can begin to condense. The cooling may occur due to contact with a cooler surface as happens in advection and radiation fogs or by ascent along frontal surfaces, up mountain- or hillsides or by convection currents. The condensation needs solid particles called condensation nuclei to be present otherwise no condensation can occur.

Dewpoint is obtained from **hygrometers**, but the level in the atmosphere that has dewpoint temperature is visible as the base of low clouds. The dewpoint and the air temperature are the same in foggy conditions.

Diurnal variation means the changes that take place during the course of a day. Wind speed, and cloudiness, follow the diurnal variation in temperature. The curves of fig. DR.6 show how the air temperature lags on the corresponding ground temperature and so comes to maximum an hour or two after local noon and reaches minimum an hour or so after dawn. The ground temperature is higher by day and lower by night and is in phase with the sun. Relative humidity is opposite, being greatest around dawn and least in the afternoon.

Whenever the wind decreases during the middle of the day against the normal

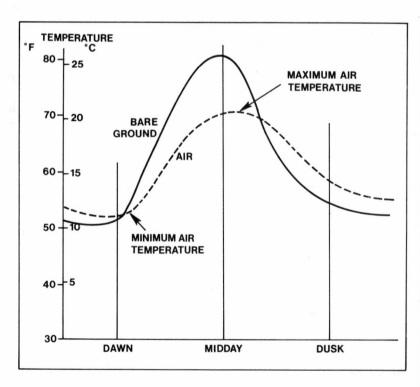

Fig. DR.6 *Curves of ground and air temperatures during a typical day in temperate-latitude summer.*

diurnal trend, the most likely causes are that the gradient has slackened or that seabreeze activity is reducing the wind.

In the tropics the diurnal variation of pressure becomes important and amounts to a daily range of some 2 mb, the maxima occurring at about 1000 and 2200 and the minima at 0400 and 1600 local time. A similar variation can be detected in temperate latitudes in quiet weather also, but in the tropics any fall of pressure that is 2–3 mb below the diurnal value is suspect and may be the first indication of the approach of a tropical cyclone. The normal diurnal ranges in latitudes 20°N to 20°S can be obtained from an Admiralty Pilot, *Meteorology for Mariners* (Ref. 11) and elsewhere.

Divergence occurs when more air leaves an air column over any place than enters it. Pressure falls at the surface. See **Pressure** and **Depressions**.

Drizzle is precipitation in which the drops are very small. It is formed by coalescence of droplets and requires a very wet airstream. Thus it is characteristic of mT airstreams and occurs in association with fog, especially in hilly districts. However, billows in a fresh to strong mT airstream can give flurries of drizzle interspersed with clearer periods. Visibility is often very poor in drizzle.

The following are the symbols used on station plots:

50	,	Slight intermittent drizzle
51	,,	Slight continuous drizzle
52	⁚	Moderate intermittent drizzle
53	⁚,	Moderate continuous drizzle
54	⁚	Intermittent dense drizzle
55	,⁚,	Continuous dense drizzle
56	⌒	Slight freezing drizzle
57	⌒⌒	Moderate or dense freezing drizzle
58	•	Slight drizzle and rain
59	•	Moderate or heavy drizzle and rain

Evaporation is the opposite of condensation and depends on two factors: (a) the temperature of the liquid surface; and (b) the kind of liquid. As water is the universal liquid, for our purposes evaporation depends only on temperature. Warm the liquid up and more molecules gain the energy to escape. The observed rate of evaporation is really the difference between the rate of evaporation and the rate of condensation back on to the water surface. The latter depends on how close to saturation the air over the surface is. With no wind the air immediately over the surface becomes very full of water vapour and so almost as many molecules drop back as evaporate. The loss consequently is small and little net evaporation occurs. However, if the air is dried out continually by the wind mixing dryer air from above with the wet air near the surface, the net evaporation increases. For this reason both temperature and wind lead to drying.

Evaporation from the wet body is the major means by which heat is lost in cases of accidental hypothermia, and it is essential to obtain shelter from wind. Without ventilation the small-craft cabin develops a 'fug', the oppressiveness of which is mainly due to the high humidity. The late K. Adlard Coles tell us in *Heavy Weather Sailing* (Ref. 14) that the worst part of being at sea in a small boat is having to put up with this oppressive fug when battened down in heavy weather. The throughput of air from ventilators is just not enough to make any appreciable inroad on the cabin humidity as the incoming air is already very high in humidity, and whatever warmth is engendered only serves to increase the degree of humidity.

Facsimile is the way that the modern transformation in weather information can be at the yachtsman's service. Actual and forecast weather charts as described in various parts of this book can make a vital difference to the convenience and safety of the sea-going yacht.

The new generation of receivers is equipped with memory stores that enable a pre-set programme of charts to be selected and printed out automatically leaving the navigator free to concentrate on other matters. Such devices are compact occupying a space less than 1 ft 6 in × 1 ft × 6 in high (45 cm × 30 cm × 15 cm) and weighing between 10 and 16 lb (4.5–7.5 kg), and they are capable of receiving signals from all the fax stations in the world when within receiving range.

The charts are broadcast at three drum speeds (also called recording rate) of 60, 90 and 120 scans per minute and the index of cooperation is either 576 or 288 lines per inch. In practice most individual stations broadcast at 120 scans per minute, but change the index of cooperation to suit the scale of the chart broadcast.

Because of the dependence of the world weather services on GMT (Z) the main synoptic hours are 0000, 0600, 1200 and 1800Z. In Europe the mental shift in converting these times to local time is not great. In the Americas it is, so the conversion to local time on page 159 applies:

In Europe, if French and Spanish are not familiar languages, then the yacht that goes south round Iberia into the Mediterranean will be without local weather forecasts as neither France nor Spain broadcasts plain-language forecasts other than in their own languages. Here facsimile would be of the greatest use and the point is clear wherever a yacht goes truly 'foreign'. The language of weather charts is universal, and the symbols and lines on the charts cross all language barriers. The establishment of the world weather service through the guiding hand of the World Meteorological Organisation (WMO) in Geneva is one of the few truly international stories of cooperation spanning all frontiers. The procedures of met. offices throughout the world follow

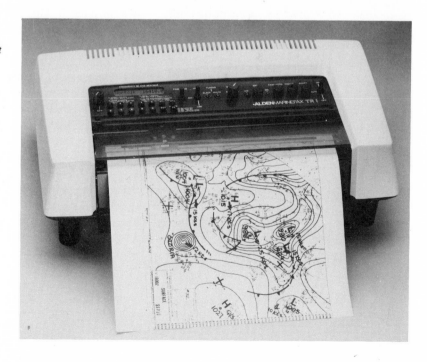

R.8   *A modern facsimile receiver which is programmable to print out automatically the charts that experience shows you that you require. This model is typical of present receivers and weighs 16 lb (7.3 kg).*

Main synoptic hour	Eastern Daylight Time	EST/CDT	CST/MDT	MST/PDT	PST
0000Z	8 p.m.	7 p.m.	6 p.m.	5 p.m.	4 p.m.
0600Z	2 a.m.	1 a.m.	Midnight	11 p.m.	10 p.m.
1200Z	8 a.m.	7 a.m.	6 a.m.	5 a.m.	4 a.m.
1800Z	2 p.m.	1 p.m.	Noon	11 a.m.	10 a.m.

the codes, symbols and chart conventions laid down in the WMO's publications. The full fax schedules are obtainable from the WMO, but abbreviated schedules are contained in Ref. 1 together with the frequencies. Obviously when stations are received on a regular basis the latest schedules can be obtained from the stations in question. Stations such as Norfolk Va issue a book describing their fax output, but not the uses to which it might be put. Some of the more go-ahead companies that make and market fax machines for yachts, such as Alden and Raytheon, supply books that help the non-specialist come to terms with the fax charts that are of use. Herein we offer suggestions as to their wider use through the utilisation of upper-air charts. In choosing a fax machine, attention should be focused on the degree of detail the reproduction system can handle. You may wish to draw your own isobars on the 'plotted points' charts and to read the station circles as these give the fastest and most exact information about individual weather elements occurring in your area. Will the machine you are looking at give you that definition? Get specimens from stations at some distance to see how the machine will cope under more adverse conditions at sea with other stations.

In European waters the facsimile stations divide the output as follows: Offenbach I – a station for land-area forecasts, etc., as opposed to Quickborn – a station with specific interest in the North Sea, the Baltic and waters surrounding Britain; Bracknell I – a 'global' station with a much deeper meteorological slant than Offenbach, as opposed to Northwood – a specifically 'naval' station whose output is directed and timed to coincide with watches at sea; Offenbach II, Bracknell II and Paris are all aircraft channels providing the continuous weather routing information for flights in Europe, the Middle East, the Atlantic and the North American continent, etc.

Suppliers of facsimile printers and related receiving gear include:

Alden Electronics, Washington Street, Westborough, MA 01581, USA
Raytheon Marine Company, 656 Island Pond Road, Manchester, NH 03103, USA
Nagrafax, c/o Hayden Laboratories Ltd, Chiltern Hill, Chalfont St Peter, Bucks SL9 9UG, England
Taiyo Musen Co Ltd, 20–7, 2-Chrome, Ebisu-Nishi, Shibuya-ku, Tokyo 150, Japan

In Britain a £5 licence is required for the reception of radio-fax. Details from Met. 0.5b Meteorological Office, Bracknell, Berks.

Fahrenheit scale Assuming that the lowest temperature obtainable by simple means was via a mixture of ice and salt, Gabriel Daniel Fahrenheit (b. 1686 in Danzig) marked it 0°F on his mercury thermometers and chose 180 degrees between ice point and steam point. Thus, with ice point at 32°F, steam point is 212°F. The scale has several advantages, among which are the fact that in temperate latitudes it rarely falls into negative figures and the degree size is almost half the Celsius or Kelvin degree which makes summer temperature sound so much better as '90 in the shade' rather than 'in the thirties Celsius'. For a conversion scale see **Centigrade**.

Floccus is a form of altocumulus associated with instability and so possible storms. See **Alto clouds**.

Fog is the most unpredictable element in weather forecasting. It is easier to see where widespread sea fog is in being from the satellite cloud pictures, but the definition of such pictures on fax machines may not enable the yachtsman to identify the areas especially when the fog is patchy or is not much different in temperature from the sea surface. The infra-red images are not as contrasty as the daylight visible passes of TIROS or the repeated images from Meteosat, GOES and other geostationary satellites. Sometimes fog appears very sharply on such pictures, however (photo R.9).

Specifically foggy areas cover the northwest Alantic and the north Pacific in summer with the highest incidence being north of 40°N. However, in Britain the east and south coasts are the most prone to fog and it follows that the continental coasts of Europe facing these will also see a fairly high incidence. Spring is particularly prone to fog at sea when sea temperatures are low but air temperatures are increasing.

Conditions favouring fog include:

(a)   air temperature higher than the sea temperature;
(b)   a long sea track (upward of 100 miles);
(c)   some wind to stir the air layers near the surface, but not enough to mix dry air aloft with the wet air near the sea and so disperse the fog;
(d)   a stable airstream indicated by flat or downward-going funnel smoke, low layer clouds, etc.

Conditions where fog is very unlikely are as follows.

R.9   *A picture that shows many of the attributes of sea fog. It may form over some areas and not over others. It sticks to the middle of the Irish Sea, but invades the northwestern coasts of Britain, Anglesea, etc. as well as the south coast of Ireland. Over the southwest and Wales it remains just off the coast rather like photo C.16.*

(a)   The sea temperature is above air temperature;

(b)   there are cumulus clouds in the vicinity;

(c)   the wind is above Force 2–3;

(d)   there is a short sea track from nearest land (30–50 miles, say).

Fog can clear when the wind shifts from a long to a short sea track and when a change occurs from an mT airstream to an mP one (passage of a front).

One of the most dangerous situations for small craft is to be fog-bound in a shipping lane. Numerous examples can be cited where, despite radar on the merchantman, yachts have been run down. If fog seems likely or is forecast, it is prudent to stay clear of the shipping lanes. Fog signals as normally carried by yachts are useless in many cases as their chances of carrying to the watch of say a large tanker are very small. The conditions of stability accompanying sea fog keep sound waves close to the water and actually help to propagate the sound further than on a clear day when the sound waves are refracted upwards and lost. Any wind will make signals from windward carry further and correspondingly less from leeward. In any case sound in fog is as capricious as the fog itself and the skipper must take note of the fact and act accordingly. See also **Radar**.

Fog in the 'present weather' position of station plots is as follows (these all refer to different aspects of fog):

40	(≡)	Deep fog in sight (deep means deeper than the height of the observer)
41	⹉	Patchy fog
42	≡|	Fog but sky visible – thinning
43	≡|	As above, sky invisible – thinning
44	≡	As 42 but no change
45	≡	As 43 but no change
46	|≡	As 42 but thickening

47	|≡	As 43 but thickening
48	⊻	Fog depositing rime – sky visible
49	⊻	As 48 – sky invisible

Föhn winds   See **Hills and mountains**

Forecasts can be obtained by various means that include the following:

DOMESTIC RADIO
land areas with some mention of coastal conditions as they affect the person on land; national coverage

special coastal waters forecasts with fishing and small craft in mind. National coverage, but local radio forecasts are the best

shipping forecasts aimed at big ships at sea. The information is mainly deep sea and little indication of coastal variations is given. Because they are designed to fit in with the watch system on merchantmen they are often inconveniently timed for yachtsmen

in the USA a 24-hour continuous set of weathercasts is broadcast by NOAA Weather Radio on one of 162.40, 162.475 or 162.66 MHz

COAST RADIO STATIONS
plain language forecasts on VHF frequencies for sea areas local to the stations several times a day. Nautical almanacs or *Admiralty List of Radio Signals* Volumes 3 and 3a (Refs 1 and 2) give details of frequencies and schedules

TELEPHONE
in Britain 'Weatherline' for land areas and 'Marineline' for coastal waters. Ask for a Telecom Guidelines Marineline card. Similar coastal forecast in France and Germany. In the USA most cities have a telephone forecast facility

TELEVISION
highly improved automated service of
satellite pictures, rainfall forecasts, and
actual and forecast chart sequences of charts
broadcast by BBC in Britain. Some ITV
regions such as Anglia TV are following
suit. This is a source of charts using what I
call the pause-and-draw method. You video
the telecast and then use the 'pause' facility
to stop the tape, clear the interference lines,
and, using a large piece of tracing paper and
a felt-tipped pen, sketch the isobars and
fronts plus a rough land outline. If you take
care to draw the isobars with some accuracy
over the area in which you are interested, a
forecast chart for not too many hours ahead
will give a pretty good idea of wind
strength and direction. You can use the
method outlined under **Pressure gradient**
to make a geostrophic scale for your chart
and so find the speed of the gradient wind.
Usually that speed will be the top of the
gusts.

Those who wish to take down the details of
the shipping forecast can buy pads of blank
charts from yacht chandlers. However,
shipping forecasts are now being broadcast
through the medium of Navtex. This
device prints shipping forecasts, gale warnings and navigation warnings automatically.

There follows an actual forecast issued at
0930 4 December 1985 from Portpatrick
Radio covering the sea areas for which is it
responsible. The format is the same trun-
cated time-saving style as used in British
shipping forecasts. With a printed forecast,
navigators around Britain may wish to try
to plot charts from this information.
Detailed instructions for doing this are
included in Ref. 9. How to plot the
information straight on to a Metmap blank
(from the Royal Yachting Association and
Royal Meteorological Society) is covered in
a simple form in the author's *Cruising
Weather* (Ref. 15).

```
-------------------------------------------
ZCZC OE65
PORTPATRICKRADIO
SHIPPING FORECAST

0930  ON 04 DECEMBER 1985

THE GENERAL SYNOPSIS AT MIDNIGHT
LOW VIKING 982 EXPECTED 150 MILES
NORTHEAST OF VIKING BY *IDNIGHT
TONIGHT. LOW 150 MILES WEST OF SHANNON
998 EXPECTED MALIN 994 BY
SAME TIME

FORECAST FROM 040700

LUNDY FASTNET IRISH SEA
SOUTH OR SOUTHWEST 4 OR 5 OCCASIONALLY
6 AT FIRST. RAIN AT TIMES.
MODERATE OR GOOD

ROCKALL
SOUTHERLY BECOMING CYCLONIC, LATER
MAINLY NORTHEASTERLY, 4 OR 5

OCCASIONALLY 6. SHOWERS. GOOD

MALIN
SOUTHWESTERLY BECOMING CYCLONIC 4 94 5
OCCASIONALLY 6.  SHOWERS.
GOOD

HEBRIDES BAILEY
MAINLY NORTHEAST 4 OR 5 OCCASIONALLY 6.
RAIN AT TIMES. MODERATE OR
GOOD

FAIR ISLE
NORTH VEERING NORTHEAST 4 OR 5
OCCASIONALLY 6 AT FIRST. SHOWERS.
GOOD

FAEROES SOUTHEAST*ICELAND
MAINLY NORTHEAST 5 OR 6 OCCASIONALLY 7
LATER. SNOW SHOWERS. GOOD

NNNN
-------------------------------------------
```

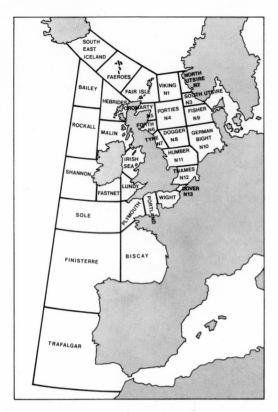

Fig. FR.1 *British sea areas as used in shipping forecasts plus the numbers of common areas used by countries surrounding the North Sea including France.*

In the US some TV weather channels exist that give continuous weather information, and some cable TV systems give a similar facility.

Dangerous-weather warnings will be broadcast at the first opportunity on domestic radio channels. In Europe this means very strong winds or very heavy rainfall, very intense thunderstorms, etc., but in the US the advisories are concerned also with the onset of hurricanes and the prospect of tornadoes.

The areas designated by each country for its own shipping forecasts differ, but some degree of commonality has been achieved. The numbers N1 to N13 in fig. FR.1 are common to most countries around the North Sea, and the same applies to fig. FR.3 around the Baltic. The French areas, other than the North Sea common ones, are shown in fig. FR.2. With these three most yachtsmen should be able to identify sea areas in Europe and the western

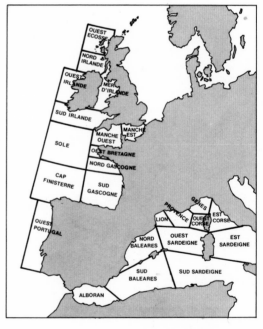

Fig. FR.2 *French sea areas excluding the common ones in the North Sea.*

Mediterranean. Wider coverage is given in the RYA booklet *Weather Forecasts* (Ref. 10), and world coverage in *Admiralty List of Radio Signals* Volume 3a, which can be obtained from major chandlers (Ref. 2).

The North American coasts are covered by the United States and Canada, as shown in fig. FR.4. The US Alaskan areas and the Canadian Northern Areas have not been shown.

Fronts appear at the major discontinuities between **airmasses** of different characteristics. The main attribute of airmasses is their over-all temperature, and thus fronts are named by the temperature of the air that will exist when the front has passed. This is good sense as the names warm front or cold front contain a simple forecast: the weather will get warmer or colder. Through learning the usual attributes of fronts the mariner will hoist in more knowledge that is important to him and the safety of his craft

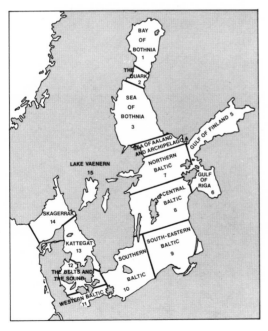

Fig. FR.3 *Sea areas common to the countries surrounding the Baltic.*

than in any other single section of meteorology. This is particularly so with regard to warm fronts, because the cloud sequence of Ci, Cs, As and finally Ns (together with Fr pannus that forms in precipitation) heralds not only the warm front or occlusion, but also the deteriorating weather that accompanies these fronts as well as the increasing wind and the windshifts that are involved.

Fronts may be in the process of formation (frontogenesis); in an active prime of life (ana-warm and ana-cold fronts) with general ascent along their surfaces, or in a state of decay (frontolysis) and the latter is usually due to the subsidence of air from aloft (kata-warm and kata-cold fronts). On the major 'trade routes' of depressions, ana fronts are to be expected with associated virulent weather, but the further from the breeding grounds the fronts travel, the weaker they tend to become. A relative few fronts may reactivate by being injected with a new airmass. Thus in continental Europe and on the eastern seaboard of Britain the majority of fronts are either occlusions or kata fronts.

Only with very active young fronts is the frontal passage a sudden change from one airmass type to the other. In later life fronts develop a more or less wide frontal zone that may take hours to pass. The front is an essential part of the development process of most depressions, but there are also frontless depressions.

See **Cold front**, **Occlusions**, and **Polar lows**.

The symbols used for warm fronts, cold fronts and occlusions will be familiar from the charts of Part One. Here are less familiar symbols found on some charts.

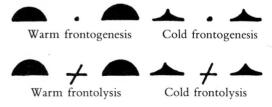

Warm frontogenesis   Cold frontogenesis

Warm frontolysis   Cold frontolysis

CANADA

ATLANTIC COAST FORECAST AREAS

1.	Fundy	23.	Southwest Coast
2.	Grand Manan	24.	South Coast
3.	Lurcher	25.	East Coast
4.	Brown's Bank	26.	Northeast Gulf
5.	George's Bank	30.	Southwestern Grand Banks
6.	Southwestern Shore	31.	Southeastern Grand Banks
7.	La Have Bank	32.	Northern Grand Banks
8.	West Scotian Slope	33.	Funk Island Bank
9.	Eastern Shore	41.	Lake Melville
10.	Sable	55.	Belle Isle Bank
11.	East Scotian Slope	58.	Sept-Isles Bank
12.	Fourchu	59.	Baie Comeau to Sept-Isles
13.	Banquereau	60.	Tadoussac to Baie Comeau
14.	Laurentian Fan	61.	Iles aux Coudres to Tadoussac
15.	Cabot Strait	62.	Quebec to Iles aux Coudres
16.	Northumberland Strait	63.	Trois Rivieres to Quebec
17.	Gulf-Magdalen	64.	Montreal to Trois Rivieres
18.	Chaleur-Miscou	65.	Gananoque to Montreal
19.	Anticosti	66.	South Labrador Coast
20.	Belle Isle	67.	Mid Labrador Coast
21.	Northeast Gulf	68.	North Labrador Coast
22.	Gulf-Port-au-Port		

CANADIAN AREAS THAT OVERLAP UNITED STATES

CANADA

PACIFIC COAST FORECAST AREAS

1. Queen Charlotte Straits
2. Johnstone Straits
3. Queen Charlotte Sound
9. West Coast Vancouver Island
16. Juan de Fuca
17. Strait of Georgia
18. Hecate Strait
19. Dixon Entrance
20. West Coast Queen Charlotte Islands
67. Bowie
68. Explorer

UNITED STATES

ATLANTIC AND GULF COAST FORECAST AREAS

1. Gulf of Maine
2. S. of Nova Scotia
3. George's Bank
4. S. of New England
5. Hudson Canyon to Baltimore Canyon
6. Baltimore Canyon to Hatteras Canyon
7. Hatteras Canyon to Blake Ridge
8. Savannah to St Augustine
9. St Augustine to Jupiter Inlet
10. Jupiter Inlet to Key Largo
11. Key Largo to Dry Tortugas
12. Cape Sable to Tarpon Springs
13. Tarpon Springs to Apalachicola
14. Apalachicola to Pensacola
15. Pensacola to Gulf Port
15a. Gulfport to Mississippi
16. Mississippi River to Intracoastal City
16a. Intracoastal City to Port Arthur
17. Port Arthur to Port O'Connor
18. Port O'Connor to Brownsville
29. Puerto Rico and Virgin Islands

UNITED STATES

PACIFIC COAST FORECAST AREAS

Coastal Areas:
1. Inland Waters of Western Washington
2. Strait of Juan de Fuca
3. Tatoosh Island to North Head
4. North Head to Point St. George
5. Point St. George to Point Arena
6. Point Arena to Point Pinos
7. Point Pinos to Point Conception
8. Point Conception to the Mexican border

Offshore Areas:
1. Cape Flattery to Cape Lookout
2. Cape Lookout to Point St. George
3. Point St. George to Point Arena
4. Point Arena to Point Conception
5. Point Conception to Guadeloupe Island

1000 FATHOM LINE

WEST CENTRAL NORTH ATLANTIC WATERS

S.W. NORTH ATLANTIC WATERS

GULF OF MEXICO
North West
East
Middle
South West

N.W. CARIBBEAN SEA

E. CARIBBEAN SEA

S.W. CARIBBEAN SEA

Fig. FR.4   *Canadian and United States sea areas excluding Northern Territories and Alaska.*

In addition there are systems that produce lines of weather that look like fronts. On weather maps these are shown as follows:

•• ▬ •• ▬   INSTABILITY LINE a batch of more than usually active showers or thunderstorms

▬▬▬▬▬   TROUGH LINES often where a set of vee-shaped isobars stick out from a low centre without a front in them

⤙⟋⟋⤙   CONVERGENCE LINE where two lots of air meet moving in opposite directions. Seabreezes on peninsulas produce convergence, and much cloud and showers can occur

Gales are referred to in shipping and other forecasts when the wind is expected to top Force-8, but for many yachtsmen Force-6 is a 'yacht gale'. Thus as the wind is bound to rise through Force-6 on its way to Force-8, the yacht skipper needs to have early warning of gales. A listening watch to a national broadcasting station such as Radio 4 (1500 m) will give early warning of possible danger. Otherwise coast radio stations broadcast gale warnings on a regular basis (see *Admiralty List of Radio Signals* Vols 3 and 3a for schedules).

Gales do not spring up without any warning. An analysis by the author at Thorney Island on the south coast of England showed that it took an average 7½ hours for the wind to rise from Force-4 (best working breeze) to Force-6 (edge of yacht gale). The shortest time was 3 hours and the longest about 10 hours. This is a guide and more exposed places than the English Channel could well see the deterioration set in more quickly.

Warnings are issued for:

GALES — if the mean wind speed is expected to increase to Force-8 (34 kt.) or more, or the gusts are expected to reach 43 kt. or more.

SEVERE GALES — if the mean wind speed is expected to increase to Force-9 (41 kt.) or more or gusts of 52 kt. or more are expected.

STORM — if the mean wind is expected to increase to Force-10 (48 kt.) or more or gusts of 61 kt. or more are expected.

The period within which the wind is expected to rise is described thus:

IMMINENT — within 6 hours of the time of issue of the forecast
SOON — 6 to 12 hours from the time of issue
LATER — beyond 12 hours from time of issue

The above is the practice in Britain, but other countries will be similar. The Pilot for a given coast will give statistical information about the gale frequencies in that locality.

Geostrophic is a term used to describe the apparent force exerted on an air parcel moving on the Earth's surface due to the latter's rotation. The effect is to throw the parcel to the right of its path in the NH and to the left in the SH. The size of the effect varies as the sine of the latitude. See **Pressure gradient**.

Gradient wind is the wind that is defined by the surface isobars. The distance apart of straight isobars gives the geostrophic wind speed, but increasing cyclonic curvature of the isobars lowers the speed which will give equilibrium with the pressure gradient. Anticyclonic curvature increases the geostrophic. The geostrophic wind modified by the curvature effect is called the gradient wind. See **Pressure gradient**.

Gusts and lulls Gusts are parcels of faster-moving air brought down from higher up and barging into the general wind. The mechanism is one where the air sinking around rising thermal currents brings the stronger wind on to the surface in chunks that may last for several minutes before passing on. Lulls are largely where the air is rising or simply where there are no gusts. The strongest gusts are due to descending upper wind being reinforced by downdraughts on to the surface which spills out like water poured on to a surface. This occurs where localised heavy rain or hail falls and so is associated with thunderstorms or very heavy showers.

The airstream over land is most variable in the morning, but is strongest in the afternoon. The extra strength cloaks the gusty variations and makes the afternoon appear less gusty. The variability begins to die out late afternoon and through the evening. Over the sea the night period may be the most variable and gusty. See also **Inversion** and **Boundary layer**.

Hail See **Thunderstorms**.

Haloes are formed by refraction in ice crystals at high altitude and they have a useful forecasting value in that the most prevalent – the 22° halo that forms about the sun or moon in Cs – is often a harbinger of deterioration and strong wind later. In Britain solar haloes are seen on average somewhere every three days, and lunar haloes are four times less frequent. This does not mean that the Cs is not present at night, but the cloud is often not thick enough to give a visible halo with the dim light from the moon. Extensive sheets of Cs form in association with jet streams and thereby predict the windward development of a low (photos C.11 and 8.1).

If a corona should replace the halo, then the cloud has thickened to As which follows Cs in the cloud sequence ahead of a warm front and the forecast of deterioration becomes more solidly based.

Other halo phenomena may at times be seen, including mock suns (photo C.11), which are patches of light either side of and at the same elevation as the sun; circumzenithal arcs which are coloured; sunpillars which are stalk-like limbs of light from a low sun towards the horizon; and a colourless horizontal halo around the zenith subtending 46° at the eye. These are the chief haloes, but there are others.

Heat lows or **thermal lows** develop over heated land areas during the middle of the day. They are fed by seabreezes very often and have more rising air in them than sinking air. Thus they become centres for the generation of thunderstorms. Pressure must be expected to fall over hot land areas during the middle of the day and to rise over adjacent cool seas at the same time. There is a trend to the opposite by night.

High cloud is going to be different forms of the ice-crystal cloud cirrus. Cirriform clouds will be white and will rarely show any shadowing. In this way they can be told from medium-level clouds which, being composed of water droplets, can become thick and so show dark areas and patches. Their height will normally lie between 20 000 and 50 000 ft, but in cold climates cirriform clouds can come close to the ground. Persistent aircraft trails look like Ci and are reported as such.

0		No cirriform clouds
1	⌐⌐⌐	Ci – not invading the sky; may or may not indicate a change (photos C.5, C.8 and C.9)
2	⌐⌐⌐⌐	Dense Ci left over from thunderstorms or heavy showers
3	⌐⌐	Dense Ci in anvil form – storms?
4	⟋	*Ci invading sky* – warm front or occlusion coming (photo C.7)

5	2―	*Jet cirrus* near the horizon – coming trouble (photo C.2)
6	⟋	*Jet cirrus* and/or Cs over most of sky – nearer to trouble (photos C.1, C.3 and C.4)
7	2⌒	*Cirrostratus* over most of sky – possible gale soon (photo C.11)
8	⌐⌒	Cs not increasing, nor over whole sky – need not mean anything
9	⟅	Cirrocumulus with maybe Ci and Cs – usually a feature of changeable weather
/		Cirrus cannot be seen

Always monitor the changes in cirriform clouds as they foretell coming weather, and in the above the shapes to look for on the station plots are in italics. Ways of doing this are described in chapters 4 and 5.

High cloud symbol appears at the very top of the station plots on weather maps.

Hills and mountains affect the wind and the weather profoundly. In hills we can include high promontories and the coastal regions where valleys run down to the sea. Among the important effects are local increases where the wind becomes constricted and this does not need two sides. Wind blowing obliquely against cliffs, etc. can increase in speed very considerably and the effects spread several miles out to sea. The effects of wind blowing over hill ridges can extend tens of miles downwind and produce contrary, even retrograde, winds. Such effects are often accompanied by lens-shaped clouds. The very variable conditions that obtain in Gibraltar harbour when the wind blows strongly from the east are well known. Much turbulence is induced by the barrier of the Rock.

Föhn effects occur when gradient winds are routed over a mountain barrier and the mountains look down to the sea. The warm, dry Föhn wind is usually not as strong as fresh to gale, but the most important factor with Föhn is a well-known psychological one which makes people very prone to accidents in the period preceding the Föhn and also when it is in being. Föhn-type winds reach their maximum on the Alpine Forelands and in the Chinook of the Rockies, but can also be experienced off the east coast of Scotland in the region of Aberdeen. They may also be in evidence on the Yugoslavian coast of the Adriatic as well as sometimes in Scandinavia. For coastal slope winds see **Mistral** and **Bora** and also **Slope winds**.

Hurricanes are the tropical cyclones of the Atlantic. They are born in warm converging air along the intertropical convergence zone (ITCZ) and so migrate northwards during the NH summer. This induces stronger geostrophic forces and the energy previously spread over a wide area becomes confined to a relatively small compass. Thus winds rise to 100–150 kn. at times and the speed of movement of 10–15 kn. at first increases to 30–35 kn. as they recurve around the sub-tropical high-pressure belt. They draw their energy from warm seas and so lose impetus when they come ashore, but hurricanes sometimes force the evacuation of coastal regions of the US as with Hurricane Diana in September 1984, which saw 100 000 people clogging roads and filling temporary shelters inland from the coasts of Carolina. Because of this, only two people died as a direct result of Diana.

The right half of the hurricane as viewed from its track is the so-called 'dangerous semicircle' and rules for avoiding this are given in all the navigation pilot books so will not be repeated here (Ref. 11). The strongest winds are found between 6 and

30 miles of the eye of the cyclone. This latter is some 6 to 12 miles in diameter and here winds are relatively light.

The difference between a tropical cyclone and an extratropical one (a depression) is that in the former the winds rotate but have to unwind into the upper westerlies. Thus the depression cannot generate the wind speed that obtains in tropical cyclones. The following terms are used to classify developments:

Tropical disturbance – a weak rotary air circulation 100–300 miles across.
Tropical depression – a surface rotation with winds below 34 kn.
Tropical storm – same as above, but winds between 34 and 63 kn.
Hurricane – a cyclone with winds of over 63 kn.

A plot of tropical cyclone tracks (fig. HR.1) shows how some start near the coast of Africa and end up as intense depressions on the Atlantic coasts of Europe. Such a one was Flossie on 16 September 1978, seen in photo R.10 crossing the North Sea. Very bad weather with wind of up to storm force can be induced by these old hurricanes demoted to depressions.

Hurricanes are given names that start with A and go on through the alphabet. The best advice for avoiding hurricanes is to listen carefully to the advisories and get to somewhere safe in plenty of time.

Hygrometers are devices for finding the relative humidity (RH) of the air. If a continuous record of humidity is required, the hair hygrograph is used. This uses the property that human and animal hair lengthens as it absorbs moisture, and through a system of levers the change can be magnified and made to actuate a pen running over a chart of RH against time. Such devices are not for use on yachts, where they will give very spurious readings.

In the wet and dry bulb hygrometer the rate of evaporation from the wet bulb depends on how humid or dry the surrounding air is. A high rate of evaporation demands the supply of latent heat from the bulb itself and so its temperature falls below that of the dry bulb. The dryer the air the greater the depression of the wet bulb and the lower the relative humidity. When the surrounding air is saturated, there is no net loss of water from the wet bulb and so it

Fig. HR.1   *The danger area for hurricanes is shown here. There is a slight risk in May, but the high month is September with August and October seeing a lesser incidence. There is still some risk in December.*

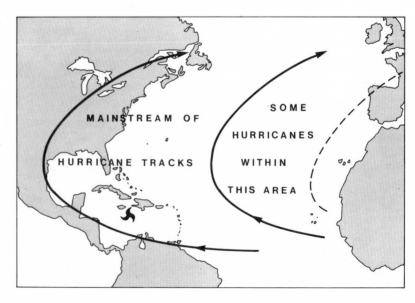

R. 10   *From space old hurricanes may not look much different from older occluded depressions (see photo 23.1 for instance). Here old Hurricane Flossie tracks across the North Sea on the evening of 16 September 1978. The weather she brought was decidedly tropical.*

reads the same as the dry bulb. The RH is then 100% and the dewpoint is the same as the air temperature.

The most practical form of hygrometer for use on a yacht is the whirling or sling type (fig. HR.2). This has two advantages in that it is small and can be stowed in a handy locker until required, and more accurate readings are obtained when air flows over the wet bulb. You normally have to buy these from a supplier of met. instruments, but some good chandlers may stock them also. See **Evaporation**.

The table overleaf is included to enable dewpoint to be obtained should you wish to use a hygrometer at sea or on land.

It might seem a good idea to buy one of the dial-type 'paper' hygrometers as sold at garden centres as they give a direct reading of RH. My experience is that they are so unreliable even on land that at sea they would be quite useless.

Inversion can be present at all altitudes and occur where the air temperature increases with height rather than lapsing with height as is the norm. In this category we can also include isothermal layers where the temperature remains constant with height. Both inversions and isothermal layers put lids on the ascent of air and so limit cloud tops. The most prevalent and important inversion

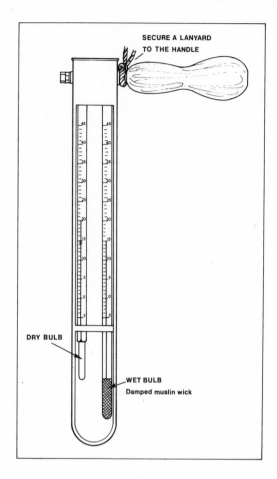

SECURE A LANYARD
TO THE HANDLE

DRY BULB

WET BULB
Damped muslin wick

Fig. HR.2 *The only truly practical hygrometer for use at sea is the whirling wet and dry bulb type. Other simpler types are unreliable. From the table it will be seen that the dewpoint is 11°C – the air is quite dry.*

is the one that forms on most nights over land. The inversion is stronger the clearer the night and the colder the surface. Thus winter nights are more likely to be calm than summer ones. Inversions prevent faster upper air from mixing with slower lower air, and so separate airstreams into decks. The wind locked away above the night inversion comes to the surface in the morning as the sun induces convection and breaks the inversion. Then the wind picks up – suddenly very often. Oceanic airstreams do not gain a night-time inversion and so winds over the sea may increase with the night compared with local land areas.

In addition there are subsidence inversions and latent heat inversions. See **Anticyclones** and **Latent heat**.

Katabatic winds sink downhill on calm, clear nights and add to landbreeze effects to produce a coastwise nocturnal wind of a few knots. Stronger katabatics descend from mountains and, if added to a sympathetic gradient, may induct fresh or even strong off-shore night-time winds. **Slope winds** are extreme forms of katabatic aided by gradient.

Kelvin scale is a scale of temperature that has absolute zero (−273°C) as its origin and a degree size that is the same as the Celsius scale. On the K scale ice point is 213.16 K and steam point 373.16 K. At absolute zero

Air temperature (°C)	Depression of wet bulb									
	1	2	3	4	5	6	7	8	9	10
Dewpoint temperatures										
0	−3	−7	−11	−18	−32					
5	2	0	−4	−8	−14	−20				
10	8	6	3	0	−3	−8	−15	−27		
15	13	11	9	7	4	1	−2	−7	−14	−26
20	18	17	15	13	11	9	6	3	0	−5
25	24	22	20	19	17	15	13	11	8	5
30	29	27	26	24	23	21	19	17	16	13

all molecular matter is inert and pressure is zero.

Land breezes blow from the land at night when conditions are otherwise quiet. They depend for their power on the difference in temperature between the land, which cools as the night progresses, and the sea, which remains the same temperature. Thus clear skies or only partly cloudy ones are important if land breezes are to blow. A land breeze may blow from any littoral low or high, but in the latter case katabatic winds will aid the speed and penetration out to sea. The summation of land breeze and katabatic is called the nocturnal wind and these winds are typically 3–5 kn. near the coastline and then lose strength in the first few miles from the shore. Such winds may be enhanced by being constricted by harbour entrances, shoreside valleys or bluff promontories. They will reach maximum frequency and strength when a mountain range exists inland from the coast. They are surface-hugging, and quite low obstructions can divert them.

The land breeze is the opposite of the seabreeze, but is usually less strong. Studies on the south coast of England have shown that the nocturnal wind usually starts before midnight, reaches its maximum around 2 or 3 o'clock in the morning and then wanes over the dawn period. Autumn and winter sailing will see more nocturnal winds than spring and summer. The cool air from the land will become convective over the sea on many occasions. Showers may even be induced as a consequence of the cool nocturnal air arriving over warmer sea.

Lapse rates are the amount that the air temperature falls off with height. When air is unsaturated it cools at the dry adiabatic lapse rate (DALR) of 5.4°F for each 1000 ft of ascent. When saturated (in cloud) it cools at half this rate at first, but the value varies with altitude. See **Adiabatic** and **Latent heat**.

Latent heat is the heat which apparently lies dormant or hidden (hence latent) in vapours, but which becomes released when the vapour condenses into liquid. The answer to the riddle of latent heat lies in the fact that the molecules of vapour are much more energetic than when they are constrained in the liquid state. The difference in their energy appears as latent heat and amounts to the release of no less than 2257 joules of heat for very cubic centimetre of water condensed. The amount of liquid water held in suspension as water droplets in clouds runs into tons, and so it follows that one of the major ways in which the air layers above the Earth are warmed is by the production of clouds. Such warmth eventually inhibits the upward growth of clouds from below and forms a temperature inversion so that the clouds stop growing. This is what happens with fair-weather Cu. The airstream in which it forms was once cold up to great heights, but immense numbers of showers that have grown in it have released so much latent heat that now there is a warm layer above the humble cumulus, and no further big Cu clouds can grow.

The converse process where liquid water evaporates into vapour entails taking in the same number of joules to remove a cubic centimetre of water. Thus puddles, etc. need sun to warm them and provide the necessary latent heat before they will disappear.

When water freezes into ice, then a smaller quantity of latent heat is released. The amount is about a seventh of that released when vapour condenses into water. A larger quantity is released when vapour transforms directly into ice (sublimation) as happens on cold days, and freezing fog forms white hoar frost on rigging, rails, etc. The process of vapour subliming directly on to ice crystals occurs in super-cooled clouds (which is the natural state) and is the major means by which snow and eventually rain are formed.

Icebergs are slow to melt as the amount of latent heat required to convert their great bulk into water is immense and is only supplied relatively slowly by the surrounding seawater. See **Rain**, **Tephigrams**.

Lightning is the result of electric charge of opposite sign being built up in different parts of clouds and in the ground or sea beneath. They are indeed giant electric sparks either from cloud to ground or from cloud to cloud. Cloud-to-ground strokes are seen as forked lightning, and many cloud-to-cloud strokes appear as sheet lightning. Sometimes a chain of lightning will travel for miles below the cloudbase of thunder clouds.

Obviously the lightning that does not reach Earth is not dangerous, hence the old truism that sheet lightning is nothing to be afraid of. It is a remarkable fact that the number of yachts that are struck by lightning is much lower than one might expect. It can happen, but seeing that a yacht is a single entity on a waste of water with a tall, mainly metal, conductor raised above it, it might seem to be a perfect target for a lightning stroke. See **Lightning conductors.**

Whereas single strokes are to be expected in temperate latitudes, groups of between 4 and 20 strokes are common in the tropics. Each stroke is dual in nature. A faintly luminous stepped-leader stroke runs down from the base of the cloud towards the ground. Each step is about 20 yards long. Along this prepared ionised track a bright, intense return stroke shoots back up to the cloud above. The effect of a stroke is to bring down negative charge to nullify the positive charge induced in the ground (see fig. LR.1). The most active storms create charge at such a rate as to allow a second-generation dart-leader stroke to travel back to earth within less than a tenth of a second after the first return stroke. This is followed by an intense return stroke which, unlike the first, is unbranched.

Fig. LR.1 *The way the charge separates in a thunder cloud leaves a preponderance of negative charge in the lower part and carries positive charge to the top of the cloud. Lightning conductors try to nullify this, but in the absence of an electric wind bluff objects can be struck whereas pointed ones may not be.*

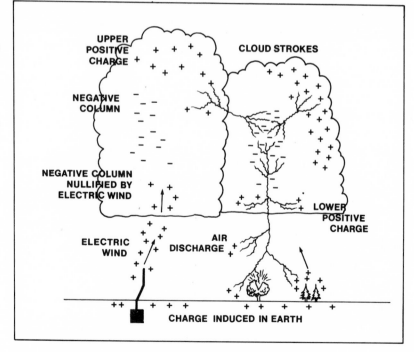

The first lightning stroke appears about 10–20 minutes after the start of any sizeable rain from a thunderstorm cell, but as cells are being born continuously during a thunderstorm, so lightning occurs continuously in different places at different times leading to the old idea that lightning never strikes the same place twice. This is not absolutely true, but anyone struck twice in the same storm is truly unlucky.

'Summer lightning' is lightning which is seen at night too far away for its accompanying thunder to be heard. As the range of the latter is typically less than 10–15 miles, such lightning indicates a storm on an adjacent coast or maybe over an island. This follows because it is heated land that generates thunderstorms.

Lightning conductors are metal points raised above the level of the building, boat, etc. to be protected. They must have a thick, preferably copper, conductor linking them to the earth or the sea and this conductor must be as straight as it is possible to make it. Owners of yachts worried about whether their craft are adequately protected should consult with good boat builders or chandlers who probably know the whereabouts of experts. Briefly there must be a large-gauge metal pathway from masthead to a metal plate in the hull below the waterline, or the keel. This is particularly important in GRP boats and those with masts stepped on deck.

The first action of a lightning conductor is to provide an 'electric wind' from the point up into the base of the threatening cloud. This, as shown in fig. LR.1, will lower the potential in the base of the cloud and may prevent a stroke. However, the constant wind of positive ions can only be fed if a good conducting path for electrons exists between masthead and sea.

If the build-up of charge in the cloud is so great as to overcome the discharging effect of the electric wind, then the conductor will allow any stroke that occurs to pass harm-

lessly to earth. The effect of bluff masthead furniture like trucks is to induce a luminous 'brush' discharge when under the intense electric fields of some thunderstorms. This is called St Elmo's Fire.

A lightning rod projecting at least six inches from the masthead above all other metal will provide a cone of protection of angle 30° to the mast. Small conductors within this protected umbrella will not be struck in preference to the major one aloft, and the angle is sufficient to cover the whole of a yacht's structure. When there is a radio antenna up there, ensure that a lightning protector is incorporated in the aerial lead or leads. You will not be able to have a lightning rod longer than the antenna so have both.

Line squalls are the accompaniment to ana-cold fronts. Lines of low black cloud are associated with a sharp rise in wind speed and very often an equally sharp wind veer (NH) or back (SH). The bar kicks up sharply, temperature falls sharply and thunder may be heard. They do not last long, but can be dangerous to small craft carrying too much sail for the new conditions and the confused seaway that results.

Local weather can vary immensely from place to place, and most of the variations are due to the topographical features over the land and to sea surface temperature variations over the sea. Air forced to ascend over rising ground creates an upward bulge in the airstream to very great heights, and clouds close to but not actually producing precipitation can get extra impetus to rain, shower, snow, etc. In thundery conditions storms will be set off by sloping ground when they do not occur on the lowlands. When thunderstorms are in being, the extra lift over hills can induce tornadoes that could conceivably move over the sea as tornado storm spouts.

Wind speeds will vary greatly from place to place, particularly when conditions are stable because of the intervention of promontories, cliffs, etc. along the coast, or valleys and hills or mountains further inland. Strange surface winds can be generated, sometimes many miles downwind of a hill or mountain barrier or by the intervention of an island. These are caused by 'rollers' in the waves that are set up in the airstream by the higher ground. Winds may temporarily blow in a direction diametrically opposite to the one prevailing at the time.

Temperature contrasts in local water temperatures can induce stronger winds and squalls in some places while other yachts only a short distance away are unaffected. Local storm corridors that occur in otherwise gale-force wind fields have been discussed in chapter 14.

The best advice in any situation is to consult the map and the Pilot to find where there is high ground upwind and do not think that you are outside the sphere of influence 30–50 miles downwind. In areas well known for strong temperature contrasts, keep a very keen weather eye for any disturbances coming across the water or oddities appearing in the clouds. It is prudent to shorten sail even if nothing comes of the phenomenon.

Low cloud has a base somewhere under 8000 ft (2.5 km). The base of fair weather cumulus is usually about 2000 ft when it first forms, but rises to 3000 ft or more by afternoon. The conventional symbols for the different types are plotted immediately below the station circle together with the number of octas and the code for the height of the base.

0		No stratus (St), cumulus (Cu), stratocumulus (Sc), or cumulonimbus (Cb)
1		Fair weather Cu (photo R.7)
2		Cu deeper than the distance base to ground. Showers later? (photo C.17)
3		Deep Cu well on the way to becoming shower clouds. If over land consider the time of day
4		Sc formed by spreading out of Cu. Air stabilising at low level
5		Sc in its own right. Usually a benign sky
6		St in a continuous layer. Could it become fog?
7		St fractus or scud of bad weather below As or Ns. The classic bad weather sky (photo C.14)
8		Sc over Cu. A generally benign sky
9		Cb with anvil plus surrounding Cb and Cu, Sc or St. Showers or thunderstorms (photo C.19)
/		Low cloud unobservable

Low cloud is, in its movement, an arrow for the direction of the gradient wind and is the direction to use with the crossed-winds rules given in chapter 5 (that is, if its base is the normal 2000–3000 ft up).

Mamma are downward-projecting bulbous areas of dark cloud usually seen on the edges of thunderstorms or big showers. They may sometimes accompany the passage of cold fronts. A good display of mammatoform clouds is not easily forgotten nor may be the intense tornadoes that accompany their appearance in America and, on rarer occasions, Europe. (Photo C.20.)

Medium cloud is different varieties of altocumulus and altostratus that occupy the middle reaches of the troposphere. Both may be due to past or present frontal activity, but the types (altocumulus castellanus and altocumulus floccus) that form in unstable atmospheres indicate thunder is a real possibility later.

0		No altocumulus (Ac) altostratus (As) or nimbostratus (Ns)
1		As through which the sun or moon appears as through ground glass. An important stage in the onset of bad weather (photo C.12)
2		As which hides the sun or moon; further into the onset of bad weather
3		Ac in one layer and thin; no definite prognostic value
4		Ac patches which are often fish-shaped and continually changing; may be part of onset of a front (photo 11.1)
5		As invading the sky and thickening. Also associated with frontal onset
6		Ac resulting from spreading of Cu or Cb. Another front coming?
7		Ac in several layers but not increasing; As or Ns may also be present (no definite prognostic value) (photo R.1)
8		Ac in lines with battlements (Ac castellanus) and/or Ac in tufts (Ac floccus); look out for thunder

9		later (photos R.2, C.22, C.23) Ac of a chaotic sky that precedes thundery outbreaks. You are nearer to thunder than 8 (photo C.24)
/		medium cloud not observed

Medium cloud symbol is plotted just above the station circle at 12 o'clock together with code figures for height. As the height of medium cloud is not of any practical use to yachtsmen, no attempt is made to explain the code.

Millibar (mb) is the standard unit of pressure measurement at present in use although there is a European movement which wishes to use the name hectopascal (hPa). The latter is just the millibar under an SI name, but there is such resistance to the move that apart from on European fax charts it is unlikely that the familiar millibar will disappear from our charts any more than thousands of feet have disappeared from aviation charts.

A bar is 10^5 pascals (Pa) and so a millibar is 100 pascals or newtons exerted over an area of one square metre. It is highly convenient as standard pressure is 1013.24 mb (760 mmHg or 29.921 inHg) and so the round 1000 mb is not much different from standard pressure and for practical purposes pressure only varies by 50 mb either side of this.

The inch of mercury is still in use on both sides of the Atlantic and so here is a conversion scale of inches into millibars.

mb	950	960	970	980	990	
in	28.05	28.35	28.64	28.94	29.23	

mb	1000	1010	1020	1030	1040	1050
in	29.53	29.825	30.12	30.42	30.71	31.01

Mirages are due to refraction of light near the surface of the Earth. Layers of heated or cooled air close to the surface produce the effects of either an inferior or a superior mirage, respectively. The inferior mirage most often encountered is the 'wet road' effect where superheated air over a road surface refracts light from the sky so that it gives the same refraction effect as a layer of water on the road. The superior mirage is very prevalent in the tropics where low coastlines appear raised above the sea with a shimmering line of light below. However, the same effect occurs in temperate latitudes when, by day, heated air travels from a distant shore. Mirages can aid landfalls in hot weather, making horizons, that might otherwise be invisible, appear as in fig. MR.1.

Mist officially finds the visibility greater than 1 km but less than 2 km and the obscuration is due to water droplets. Haze has similar limits, but the obscuration is due to dry particulates such as dust, smoke, etc. In shipping forecasts the word 'smoke' is used to denote haze.

Mistral is the strong to gale-force slope wind of the Gulf of Lions. It is particularly strong in the Rhone valley and so across the coastlands comprising the Rhone delta. Force-8 mistral can occur somewhere between Perpignan and Marseilles in most

months of the year with a maximum in March and a minimum in August–November. Gradient wind from the north induces strong mistral, and even in the low-incidence months Force-6 mistral blows somewhere on an average six days of the month. It loses its ferocity as it moves offshore.

Mixing is a most important concept to the understanding of surface wind. Except when surface inversions exist, the turbulent surface wind is always being mixed with less turbulent, but stronger, wind from a deck a few thousand feet thick above it. This mixing of stronger wind with slower surface wind is what starts the latter moving on calm mornings. The mixing depth deepens as the degree of heating increases and so, as the wind tends to be stronger higher up, the wind increases into the afternoon. When the mixing is inhibited by the land cooling below the air temperature, then the wind dies too as is well known in late afternoon. Mixing also contributes **gusts and lulls** to the wind.

Mixing of very moist calm air with dryer air above can induce sudden clamps of fog, but equally a strengthening wind can mix dryer upper air with foggy air and so clear existing fog. See **Fog** and **Boundary layer**.

Fig. MR.1 *The way superior (upper) and inferior (lower) mirages are formed.*

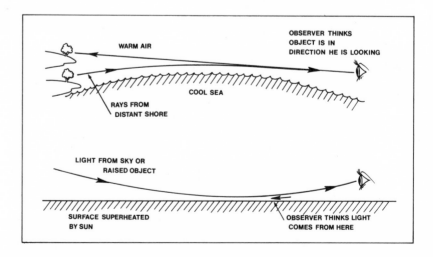

WARM AIR

OBSERVER THINKS OBJECT IS IN DIRECTION HE IS LOOKING

COOL SEA

RAYS FROM DISTANT SHORE

LIGHT FROM SKY OR RAISED OBJECT

SURFACE SUPERHEATED BY SUN

OBSERVER THINKS LIGHT COMES FROM HERE

Navtex is an international service controlled by the International Marine Organisation (IMO) which gathers navigation and weather information from all sources and rebroadcasts it at regular intervals on 518 kHz. At the time of writing it covers most of Europe, the eastern seaboard of the United States and the Gulf of Mexico and surrounding areas. It will eventually be a worldwide service giving coverage up to 200 miles offshore. The messages are received automatically by a special receiver-printer and give a plain-language telex printout in English. The information covers hazard warnings, gale warnings, ice reports, nav-aid-systems information, search and rescue alerts, plus standard weather forecasts. See **Forecasts**.

Nephanalysis is an interpretation of a satellite cloud image by an expert giving the cloud types, their amount and distribution. For many people, including, we might add, many meteorologists, a nephanalysis is essential in interpreting the clouds seen.

The cloud symbols used are those to be found under **Low cloud**, **Medium cloud** and **High cloud** but the following special symbols are used on charts including ones involved in the weather-routing of ships.

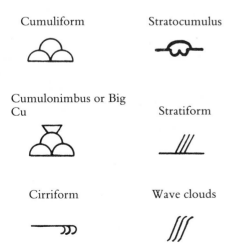

Cumuliform   Stratocumulus

Cumulonimbus or Big Cu   Stratiform

Cirriform   Wave clouds

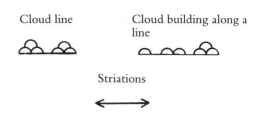

Cloud line   Cloud building along a line

Striations

Cloud amount is described in the following self-evident code: O = Open = less than 20% covered; MOP = Mostly open = 20–50%; MCO = Mostly covered = 51–80%; C = Covered = over 80% covered.

Cloud boundaries

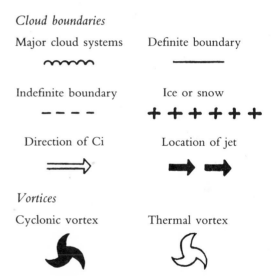

Major cloud systems   Definite boundary

Indefinite boundary   Ice or snow

Direction of Ci   Location of jet

Vortices

Cyclonic vortex   Thermal vortex

Nimbostratus (Ns) is the rain-bearing cloud of bad weather. It is often solid for thousands of feet, and below its true base a form of stratus (pannus) forms which in driving rain forms the low amorphous cloudbase experienced. Fog is sometimes formed below the pannus layer over the sea, and both fog and pannus are due to excessive humidity below the cloudbase. Ns is particularly associated with cold and warm fronts and produces most of the continuous rain we experience. Sometimes cumulonimbus grows within the Ns mass and produces showers with the more continuous rain. This usually means an ana-cold front is passing. (Photo C.14.)

Nimbus means rain-bearing and so stratus that rains is nimbostratus and cumulus that rains is cumulonimbus (not nimbo-cumulus!).

Nocturnal winds   See **Land breezes**.

Occlusions are fronts in the later stages of the life-cycle of depressions where the cold front has caught up the warm front and lifted the warm air off the ground. The function of the major atmospheric processes is to transport warm air aloft. Showers do it by convection and the release of latent heat, and fronts do it by lifting warm air over cold and also releasing latent heat. As fig. OR.1 shows there are two forms of occlusion depending on whether the air behind the front is colder than that ahead (cold occlusion) or the reverse (warm occlusion). The occlusion process goes with the filling phase of the depression life-cycle but new low centres are prone to develop on points of occlusion and take over from the original centres.

Weather associated with occlusions is not likely to be as bad as with young vigorous ana-warm and cold fronts. There is no warm sector and so no mT air with its attendant sea fog risk.

The following are used on weather maps:

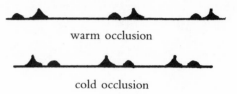

warm occlusion

cold occlusion

Past weather is the weather in the past hours and is plotted at four o'clock from the station circle on weather maps. The period is the preceding six hours at the main synoptic hours of 0000, 0600, 1200 and 1800 GMT. It is the preceding three hours at the intermediate hours of 0300, 0900, 1500 and 2100 GMT. Weather in the past hour also appears in the **present weather** position on station circles.

Fig. OR.1   *There are two kinds of occlusion. The cold occlusion (upper) has colder air behind it than in front, and the warm occlusion (lower) is the opposite. Both lift the warm air off the surface.*

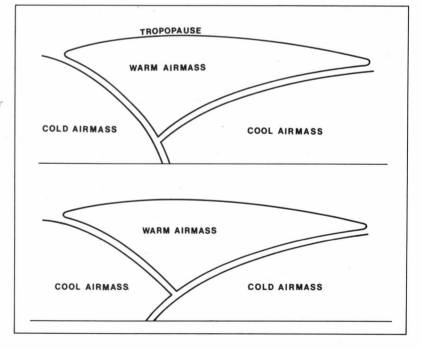

0	○	Less than half cloud cover during the period
1	◑	More than half cloud cover for part and less than half cover for the rest
2	◐	More than half cloud cover for the period
3	⇌/	Sandstorm, duststorm or blowing snow
4	≡	Fog or thick haze
5	,	Drizzle
6	●	Rain
7	*	Snow
8	▽	Shower
9	⎍	Thunderstorm(s) with or without precipitation

Finding shower symbols, for example, in both present and past weather positions indicates more than isolated shower activity unless of course the shower started just before the time of observation and is continuing.

Past weather in the preceding hour is plotted in the present weather slot of the station circle as follows:

20	,]	Drizzle that is not freezing
21	●]	Rain that is not freezing
22	*]	Snow
23	●*]	Sleet
24	∼]	Freezing drizzle or rain
25	●▽]	Rain showers
26	*▽]	Snow or sleet showers
27	▵▽]	Rain and/or hail showers
28	≡]	Fog
29	⎍]	Thunderstorm

Pileus is an eyebrow-shaped cap of cloud that appears over the heads of rapidly growing cumulus clouds. Observation of pileus indicates very rapid convection and so the prospect of showers or even thunderstorms soon. You can often see these wisps left behind by the fast-growing cloud and so existing further down. Skeins of this cloud are very evident in the centre and on the right of photo C.19. They have been left behind by the rapidly growing tops.

Polar lows are frontless whirls of air that can produce some of the most abysmal weather out of season. They are filled with cold, wet air, and heavy showers occur together with more continuous rain. These lows come down from cold northern seas in the edges of blocking anticyclones whose centres lie to the east somewhere. They can be slow moving and may take days to clear.

Precipitation is a collective word for all the various types of rain, snow, hail, etc. See **Drizzle**, **Rain**, **Snow**, **Hail**, **Sleet**.

Present weather is the weather occurring at the observing station at the time of observation which is about 10 minutes to the hour. The code for reporting it is complex, but the symbols will appear on weather charts and so are given under their respective heads. The descriptions given are simplified to provide only essential information that may be of use. The code figures will be two in number and 00 through to 19 all refer to phenomena whose form will be evident from the following:

ww	0	1	2	3	4
0	○	⊖	-⊖-	Ò	⁓
1	=	= =	= =	⦓	☺

5	6	7	8	9
∞	S	$/ℓ	Ɛ	(⇌)
)●(	(●)	⎍	∀	)(

00	Cloud not observed	12	Continuous shallow fog
01	Cloud decreasing	13	Lightning seen but no thunder heard
02	Cloud remaining much as it was		
03	Cloud increasing	14	Precipitation in sight but not reaching ground
04	Visibility cut by smoke, forest fires etc.		
		15	Same as above but reaching ground or sea surface
05	Haze		
06/	These two refer	16	Same as above but close to station
07	to dust in the atmosphere		
		17	Thunderstorm but no precipitation
08	Dust devils		
09	Dust or sandstorm		
		18	Squalls now or in the past hour
10	Mist (visibility between 1000 and 2000 m)		
		19	Funnel clouds now or in past hour
11	Patches of shallow fog		

All the 20–29 symbols refer to **past weather**

All the 30–39 symbols refer to duststorms, sandstorms or blowing snow

40–49 refer to different aspects of **fog**

50–59 refer to different aspects of **drizzle**

60–69 refer to different aspects of **rain**

70–79 refer to different aspects of **snow**

80–99 refer to different aspects of convective weather from **showers** through to **thunderstorms**

Pressure is the force exerted on a unit area by the atmosphere. It acts equally in all directions and is basically due to the constant bombardment of the surface by immense numbers of molecules. Pressure increases when

(a)   the number of molecules increases; or

(b)   the speed of the molecules increases as a whole, i.e. the temperature increases; or

(c)   both these things happen at the same time.

The meteorological process that varies (a) is called **divergence** when it reduces the number of molecules in an air column and

convergence when it increases it. Pressure must also fall at the surface when lighter (warmer) air arrives to replace denser (colder) air and vice versa. Thus one contribution to a low-pressure area is warm air replacing cold air aloft, but divergence is also a major contributory factor.

Pressure gradient is the amount (in mb) that the atmospheric pressure at the surface falls with distance. If a larger number of isobars can be fitted into a given distance, the gradient is said to be 'tighter', and tighter gradients bring stronger winds.

The wind at 2000 ft follows the isobars, and if we call the pressure gradient G millibars per mile (or kilometre), then it can be shown that when the tendency for the air to flow down the gradient from higher to lower pressure equals the geostrophic force trying to throw it to the right of its path (NH)

$$G = 2\,\omega\,d\,v\,\sin\phi \qquad (1)$$

where ω = angular speed of Earth (which is fixed), d = air density (changes in which can be ignored), v = wind speed, and ϕ = the latitude. So as ω and d do not change

$$\frac{G}{v\,\sin\phi} = \text{a constant quantity} \qquad (2)$$

Once we fix the isobar spacing, say at 4 mb between isobars, then

$$G = \frac{4}{L} \qquad (3)$$

where L is the distance over the ground between the isobars. Thus GL is constant also and we can extract the vital formula that shows which are the important quantities involved. This is

$$v\,L\,\sin\phi = \text{constant} \qquad (4)$$

(a)   Fixed latitude ϕ: $v\,L$ = constant so that as wind speed goes up L has to go down to keep the product of the two quantities constant.

(b)   Fixed wind speed v: $L\,\sin\phi$ = constant

so that in low latitudes (when sin φ is small) the distance L between the isobars has to increase and becomes infinite at the equator).

At 50°N or S the distance L that, at 4 mb intervals, represents a wind speed of 10 kn. is 300 nautical miles (555 km). This fact enables us to construct a geostrophic wind scale to measure the speed of the wind from the isobar spacing. The weather chart will have a scale on it (if not figs PR.1 and PR.2 will serve the same purpose). Take a piece of transparent plastic sheet and mark off from an origin line O (fig. PR.3) a distance of 300 Nm. This will represent 10 kn. wind speed. Double this distance for 5 kn. and halve it for 20 kn; halve again for 40 kn., etc. To mark any speed on the scale measure the distance from origin O to the 10 kn. mark. Call the distance X. Then $10X$ is always the same. If x is the distance corresponding to speed v, $vx = 10X$. Example: if we want to mark 25 kn. then $25x = 10X$ and $x = 0.4X$, etc.

If you want to scale for isobars at 8 mb then double the distances corresponding to each wind speed, and if at 2 mb intervals halve the distances. This is evident from the inset scales on figs PR.1 and PR.2.

Examples of how to use the scales will be found in chapter 21, but note that in

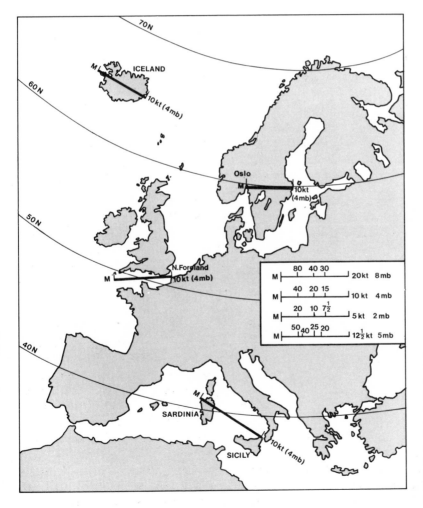

Fig. PR.1 *If you have a chart without a scale on it (as, for example, when using the video pause-and-draw method advocated under Forecasts), then you can make a geostrophic scale on any latitude by taking the given distances off the chart. If the isobars are at other intervals use the inset markings.*

Fig. PR.2 *This does the same for North America as fig. PR.1 does for Europe and the Mediterranean.*

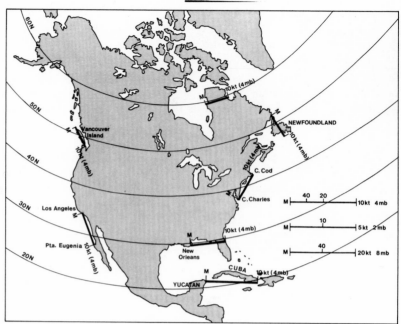

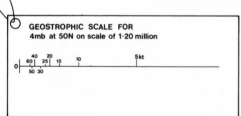

Fig. PR.3 *What your geostrophic scale should look like when you have made it.*

latitudes other than 50°N the distance corresponding to 10 kn. is as follows:

Latitude	Distance in Nm
70	245
60	265
50	300
40	360
30	460
20	670

If you use the pause-and-draw method outlined under **Forecasts**, you will have a chart without a scale. However, you can make a geostrophic scale very easily using the geographic distances shown in figs PR.1 and PR.2. You do not need to be too accurate over this as the errors introduced by other factors will outweigh the slight errors in the scale you have made.

Radar is increasingly being used for local weather forecasting in the short term. The ability of radar to see rain, especially heavy rain, combined with the pictures from geostationary satellites, is used to provide instant weather warnings of sudden deluges, the outbreak of heavy thunderstorms, etc.

In the United States the kind of radar information available is shown in fig. 22.2 and in Britain a radar network is being installed to allow 'nowcasting' and short-period forecasts of rainfall up to as much as six hours ahead. Radar has shown that the speed with which shower clouds move is about the same as the speed of the highest gusts from them, and observations made during the night of the Fastnet storm showed that the radar could foretell the maximum gusts over wide areas. The

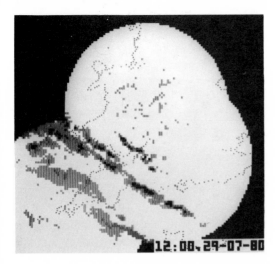

12:00, 29-07-80

R.11 *A radar image of showery troughs advancing northeastwards across south-west and southern England and Wales. The bulbous lobe shape of the picture* *reflects the limit of the radar coverage. (Photo by courtesy of the Meteorological Office, Radar Research Laboratory, Malvern, UK.)*

present problem is how to get this information to yachtsmen.

Typical results of the British radar coverage are shown in photo R.11. Thunderstorms producing very heavy rainfall are working their way across the Bristol Channel and towards the Solent area. Under these darker echoes are heavy gusts and locally torrential rain which can temporarily blot out landmarks and seamarks.

Radiation is the emission of heat energy from bodies through the medium of electromagnetic waves. The hotter the body the further towards the violet end of the spectrum do the wavelengths of maximum intensity move. Thus the sun radiates as if its temperature were 6000° K and transmits maximum energy at visible wavelengths, peaking in the middle of the spectrum at the green wavelength of 555 nanometres (nm). The Earth on the other hand radiates on average as if it were at around 300° K or less, and as the rate of emission depends on the temperature raised to the fourth power, it is obvious that the sun's emission completely dwarfs that of the Earth (or any other planet). Thus on the sunlit side, the Earth receives radiation from the sun and at the same time loses it back to space. When the rate of absorption equals that of emission, then the temperature will become maximum. This occurs a couple of hours after local noon after which the outgoing radiation exceeds the incoming and the Earth cools through the night period until the morning intake of radiation from the rising sun again exceeds the loss from the cold Earth and the temperature of the soil begins to rise again. The air temperature lags on the soil temperature and is minimum about an hour after dawn. See **Diurnal variation**.

The sea gains its radiational energy in depth and so does not show a diurnal variation as the land does. It is continuously radiating heat, but gaining it from the above radiation plus mixing of warm edge water on coasts with cooler deep water as tidal streams carry the latter out to sea. The sea reaches its minimum temperature in February (NH) and its maximum in July/August; in the SH it is the opposite. Within the tropics there is much less variation in sea temperature with season.

In winter overnight radiation from drying banks, flats, etc. provides a means by which the warmer flood waters can become very chilled leading to the appearance of ice floes in creeks and harbours. The deep sea never freezes in the temperate latitudes and any ice found in it must have 'calved' from much colder regions.

Over the sea, radiation has little effect on surface air temperature, but over land and surrounding creeks, harbours, etc., the overnight cooling can lead to radiation fog by morning. Such fog burns off with the sun when the latter is high enough in the sky, but cloud cover that comes in over a fog layer can make the latter persist. Shallow fog may exist over creeks, etc. due to drainage of air from the land overnight and may be the only fog there is. This usually clears not by heating but by being mixed with dryer air above it as the wind gets up.

Direct radiation from the sun will warm people and objects but does not have a direct effect on air temperature. A thermometer in the sun will register a temperature that bears no relation to the true air temperature. The latter is only truly found in the white louvred boxes called Stevenson's screens and then the height of the bulb must be 4 ft above the ground. None of these precautions is likely to be exactly obtainable on a yacht. If you want the air temperature, keep the thermometer in a shaded corner of the craft that is not in the hot efflux from the galley nor the fug of the cabin.

Rain is described as light, moderate or heavy and may be continuous, intermittent or occasional. Rain as a description tends to refer to the precipitation from layer clouds which are forming fronts or were part of fronts. However, not all such rain is frontal, especially in hilly areas, and on windward slopes orographic uplift can produce continuous rain or drizzle that can go on for days on end. Most winter rain is of the continuous kind, whereas much of it in spring and summer is showery. Rain, for the yachtsman, is not of itself a hazard – you just get more wet. It is the meteorological message that is important. In essence continuous rain means frontal activity of some kind whereas drizzle need not mean that – only that the cloud is thick enough to produce small drops. Continuous rain that is persistent, starts light and increases to moderate means:

(a)   a warm front or occlusion;
(b)   a change of airmass to come;
(c)   fog if the airmass to come should be maritime Tropical or a derivative of it (warm front only);
(d)   possibly being under the cloud shield

surrounding a low centre (cyclonic wind changes – you should note major changes in the log – can help sort this one out);
(e)   showers to come if the front should be an occlusion (see remarks under **Occlusions**).

True rain cannot fall from shallow clouds. This is because the major rain-making processes occur above where the temperature in the clouds has fallen to below −13°C (9°F). Minute ice particles at these levels gobble up supercooled water droplets which coexist with them and so grow into large ice crystals and so into snow flakes. These flakes fall against the rising air that is forming and maintaining the cloud. When they get below the freezing level (0°C or 32°F) they can melt to raindrops. No raindrop of any size could survive if it were not for the snow 'parachutes' that lower them relatively near to the ground before they become water drops. Really large 'thunder spots' need also to be electrically charged. This gives them cohesion and prevents them from being torn apart by friction as they fall. Rain on the windscreen that is of several different sizes has probably started as big drops and these have ruptured on the way down.

Rain can fall from 'warm' clouds, especially in the tropics, but the process is then one of growth by collision. It has become increasingly evident that this process goes on in the temperate latitudes as well. However, again neither large raindrops nor heavy rain can be induced by droplets colliding with one another and coalescing. The coalescence process is the only one that can produce drizzle. Conversely deep clouds do not produce drizzle.

Rain is composed of drops whose size is greater than half a millimetre and falls mainly from nimbostratus and altostratus clouds. Drizzle is fine drops whose size is less than half a millimetre and that fall from low clouds like stratus and stratocumulus.

Freezing rain (or drizzle) is a hazard of winter sailing because the drops freeze on impact with all the top hamper of a yacht and can make it dangerously top-heavy unless cleared using chipping hammers.

All these refer to aspects of rain:

60	●	Intermittent slight rain – old fronts usually
61	● ●	Continuous slight rain – beginnings of a warm front or occlusion rainfall
62	● (stacked)	Intermittent moderate rain – usually from occlusions and older fronts
63	● ● ●	Continuous moderate rain – what we expect from warm fronts, cold fronts and occlusions
64	● ● ● (stacked)	Intermittent heavy rain – not normally associated with normal fronts. Can be old fronts that have become unstable
65	● ● ● ●	Continuous heavy rain – often from cold fronts, polar lows and the cloudbursts that follow afternoons of thunderstorms
66	∿	Slight freezing rain – rather special conditions with surface temperatures below zero
67	∿●	Moderate or heavy freezing rain – very dangerous as it leads to heavy accretions of clear ice, possibly to glazed frosts, etc.
68	● ✳	Slight sleet – snow falling into warmer air near the ground
69	✳ ● ✳	Moderate or heavy sleet – heavier snow falling into warmer air near the ground

Relative topography You will not come across this term unless you have a fax machine. It refers to the thickness of the air between two standard pressure levels, and the most often used levels are 1000 and 500 mb. Thickness has important things to say to professional meteorologists but is not of importance to yachtsmen.

Satellites used for met. purposes are of two kinds, polar orbiting and geostationary. Those in geostationary orbit (GSO) are spread round the 35 786 km (a little under 20 000 Nm) height at which any body orbits at the same angular speed as the Earth. They effectively cover the whole of the Earth's surface (fig. SR.1). See extra information in chapter 23.

The polar orbiters are TIROS (television infra-red orbital satellite) type satellites and how they effectively cover the Earth's surface is shown in fig. SR.1 from a height of 900 km (a little less than 500 Nm) in circular orbits that take 101 minutes to complete. The National Oceanic and Atmospheric Administration (NOAA) have NOAA 6, 7, 8 and 9 covering the Earth at the time of writing, and the USSR has similar Meteor satellites doing the same job, but only in the visible. This means that unlike the NOAA satellites they cannot obtain cloud images at night. The infra-red and visible pictures are broadcast simultaneously and can be received by automatic picture transmission (APT) on ordinary non-directional dipole aerials.

Most of the images seen on TV are from satellites in GSO, and any shown in time-

Fig. SR.1   *The two kinds of met. satellite orbit are shown here. The combination of Earth rotation and TIROS orbit yields a snaking satellite shadow.*

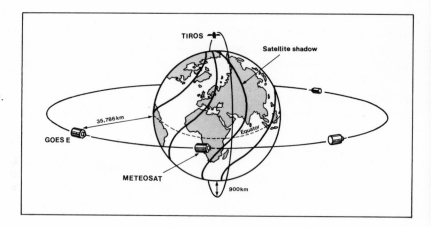

lapse sequence must be because the interval between pictures is half an hour for GSO whereas it is twice a day for TIROS. However, TIROS images are not distorted by the curve of the Earth as those from GSO satellites are. The latter can, however, be corrected to give the same overview as TIROS.

The data sent back by both forms of satellite include cloud cover, sea and land surface temperatures, sea state, limits and types of ice and snow cover, etc., and information from data collection platforms (DCPs) can be interrogated by the GSO satellites. The DCPs are automatic stations spread over land and sea that will respond to signals from the satellite and so provide information on a specific weather event that has been shown up perhaps by the satellite's own images.

Sources of these pictures are of course the routine TV weather formats, but it is now possible to interface a home computer with simple software that will enable anyone sufficiently interested to display directly on their domestic TV the pictures from the NOAA APT system. Only highly expensive equipment as yet exists to receive the GSO pictures. The TIROS images in this book are by the Department of Electronics and Electrical Engineering, The University, Dundee, Scotland, unless otherwise stated.

Sea state is plotted below the station circle and the code figures include sea surface temperature, wave period and wave height. In addition a wavy black line indicates the wave direction. This is in many ways the only symbol that is important when reading ship reports on actual charts. Otherwise wave height analyses and prognoses are broadcast regularly from fax stations and could be of crucial value when setting off into green water. Sea temperature analyses are made on a routine basis by satellite observation. See **Station circle** and chapter 16.

Seabreeze is a wind generated by the differential heating of the land adjacent to water. It usually starts in the morning, continues through the afternoon and dies in the evening. Its throw may be 50 miles inland and 30 miles out to sea in temperate latitudes, extending further in the tropics. Breezes may occur on quiet days during most months of the year rising to a maximum frequency in May–June in temperate localities. More information is in chapter 20 and Refs 8 and 9.

Secondary depressions occur from the growth of waves on the trailing cold fronts of primary depressions. On their polar sides they may easily lower the wind speed but on their equatorial sides the gradient is squeezed by the insertion of low pressure, and stronger gales are induced than occurred with the primary. Intelligent use of the crossed-winds rules and observation of the sky will usually alert the watch to the fact that the jet stream is staying W or NW and not curving in from SW as it should if a ridge is following. (For SH read SW for NW, and vice versa.)

Showers occur when the airstream is colder than the surface over which it travels. It then gains heat from the surface, and convection currents start which cool as they ascend so that cloud appears at the condensation level when the temperature has fallen to dewpoint. Small cumulus clouds are prevented from rising very far by stable layers above them, but when the upper air is cold, the rising currents may not stop rising until they are 10 000 to 20 000 ft or more. These are deep enough to produce heavy showers. The clouds are then called cumulonimbus and they may or may not develop anvil tops. Hail is often an accompaniment to the rain of heavy showers especially in spring and summer. Thunder may also occur but is not necessarily going to do so.

Showers of rain do not cut visibility greatly, or, if an intense one does, the obscuration is fairly short-lived as the life-cycle of most showers is of the order of half an hour in their prime. They are also travelling over you at more than gradient speed so should not last long. Passing showers in otherwise blue skies lead to the weather saying 'A sunshiny shower won't last half an hour.' The following symbols appear in the 'present weather' slot of station plots:

80		Slight rain shower(s)
81		Moderate or heavy rain shower(s)
82		Violent rain shower(s)
83		Slight sleet shower(s)
84		Moderate or heavy sleet shower(s)
85		Slight snow shower(s)
86		Moderate or heavy snow shower(s)
87		Slight showers of snow or rain with graupel
88		As above but moderate or heavy
89		Slight hail showers with or without sleet or rain. See codes 90–99 under **Thunderstorms**

SI (Système Internationale) is the scientific, self-consistent set of units and dimensions based on the metre, kilogram, second and ampere as basic units. It is also known as the MKSA system from these unit names. In SI units pressure is in pascals (Pa) and force in newtons (N) so that as the acceleration due to gravity is very close to 10 m/s^2 a kilogram exerts a force of about 10 N. Thus normal atmospheric pressure is about 100 000 Pa which is also a bar and therefore the atmosphere exerts a force on each square kilometre equal to about 10 tonnes (a tonne is roughly equivalent to a ton). The professional met. services have generally standardised on SI units modified for their special purposes, but long usage of the traditional units means that it is by no means a universal system.

Sleet is a mixture of rain and snow and occurs when a warm layer exists near the ground so that falling snow partially melts on the way down.

Slope winds When sailing coasts where mountains rise from the sea, beware of falling winds especially if there should be any snow visible on the tops. These winds, which may grow to gale force quite rapidly, are partly over-sized **katabatics**, but reach maximum strength when the gradient is also for winds from over the ridges. The most infamous slope winds are the **mistral** of the Gulf of Lions and the **bora** of the Adriatic. Lesser slope winds will be experienced from high coasts which do not necessarily have to be mountains high. They are associated with cold fronts, i.e. cold air suddenly arriving. When the wind is warm then *Föhn* effects are felt.

Snow will invade both ends of the normal sailing season, and those who sail through the winter in the temperate latitudes will have to contend with it. The greatest hazard at sea comes from the way snow cuts visibility. Spring snow showers can suddenly white-out marks, land and other ships, and such showers can go on until as late as May with greater risk the further north you go.

Under **rain** it is said that all moderate or heavy rainfall starts off as snow in deep clouds and melts below the freezing level. When the latter is close to sea level the snow never melts. Further, in snow all that falls survives to the surface unlike rain where small drops may never reach the ground as they evaporate away to nothing on the way down. Thus snow showers may take on the characteristics of more continuous precipitation as the snow starts ahead of the shower clouds and tails off behind them. It fills the space between one shower and the following one, again unlike rain showers where there are more distinct gaps between the showers.

When the air is very cold, snow pellets fall. These are often called *soft hail* or *graupel* and are white, opaque grains of ice with a diameter between 2 and 5 mm. The cloud involved is cumulonimbus. Sometimes *snow grains* fall and this is often described fairly accurately as 'sago snow'.

All the following refer to different aspects of snow or other solid precipitation.

70	✱	Intermittent snow – slight
71	✱ ✱	Continuous slight snow
72	✱ (stacked)	Intermittent moderate snow
73	✱✱✱	Continuous moderate snow
74	✱ (stacked)	Intermittent heavy snow
75	✱✱ (stacked)	Continuous heavy snow
76	⟷	Diamond dust
77	—△—	Snow grains
78	—✳—	Isolated star-like snow crystals
79	△ (dotted)	Ice pellets

Stability and instability refer to the tendency of air displaced upwards to sink again (stability) or to go on rising (instability). Cold air decks over warm ones or surfaces are unstable. In the very simplified fig. SR.2 the environmental lapse rate curve (solid) is such that air cooling at the dry adiabatic lapse rate and then at the saturated adiabatic lapse rate produces instability because at all heights up to where they meet, the air in the rising air parcels is warmer than outside. It is thus less dense and rises as a bubble does in water. Another, more intense, situation of the same kind is illustrated under **Tephigram**. Above the cloud top in these figures the air deck is stable as rising air will cool below the surroundings and so will become more dense and sink again.

Air near the ground goes stable during late afternoon or evening because of the

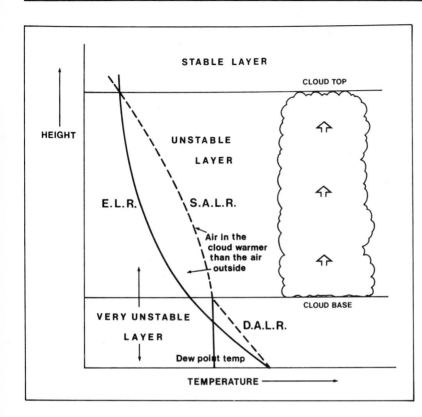

Fig. SR.2 *The basics of cloud growth. The air falls off in temperature along the environmental lapse rate (ELR) which continually varies. The air cools at the lapse rates. When it cools to dewpoint cloud forms. When it cools to the ELR temperature the cloud stops. The ELR near the ground is 'super-adiabatic' and that means high instability.*

cooling of the ground (see fig. SR.3). This effectively confines the surface air deck to the ground and *mixing* cannot occur so that the surface wind goes quiet overnight. No such thing will occur over the sea, and in the transition zone between land and water the wind often increases. See also **Fog**, **Showers**, **Thunderstorms**, **Inversion**.

Station circle is the position of a station on the weather map which is ringed by the observations made there in the manner indicated.

For forms and descriptions of clouds see **high**, **medium** and **low clouds**. Present weather symbols are found with **Rain**, **Showers**, etc. For tendency, see **Barometric tendency**. Visibility code: for figures up to 50 multiply by 100 m, i.e. 31 = 3.1 km; for 56–80 give km thus: 57 = 7 km, 64 = 14 km, etc.

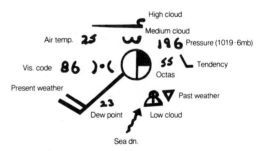

Stations Weather stations are all given numbers and a geographic prefix to tell you which country is involved. They change with time as airfields, etc. close or change their status. The full list is in *Admiralty List of Radio Signals* Vol. 4 (Ref. 3). As examples London Airport (Heathrow) is 03772 (03 for Britain), Helgoland is 10120, Gander International Airport is 71803 and San Francisco International Airport is 72494.

Only a few stations are designated as

Fig. SR.3 *How to read meaning into a Stüve diagram.*

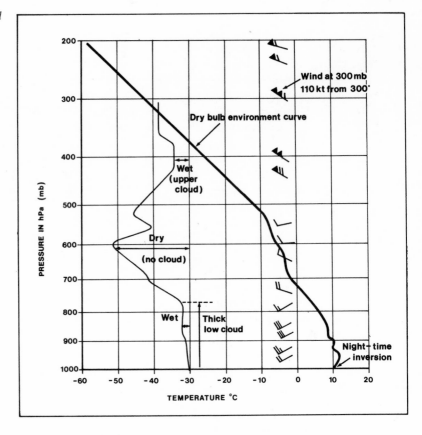

public service stations and are shown in the phone book. These, together with weather centres, bureaux, etc., are the ones to ring if you wish to talk to a forecaster. Coastguard stations can give present weather as they observe it, but can only reiterate official forecasts.

Stüve diagram is a thermodynamic diagram serving the same purpose as a **tephigram** and is favoured by some European countries. Stüve diagrams are regularly broadcast from the Offenbach I fax station and this is the only way the mariner is likely to meet them. Like the tephigram they are of immense help to the professional meteorologist, but their use for the yachtsman is limited. They could be of great help to the dedicated amateur who cares to learn the rules of using such diagrams, but the majority will not wish to go that far.

However, some of the useful attributes can be culled from fig. SR.3. The diagram plots pressure against temperature of the air as read by radiosonde ascents. The main curve that goes off to the left gives the ordinary air temperature. The wetness of the air is plotted as a difference from the ordinary temperature from a line drawn arbitrarily up the −30°C line. The figure indicates how to read meaning into the plot. Upper wind direction and speed are also plotted.

Subsidence is a technical term meaning the sinking of a body of air as a whole. It is pronounced 'sub-sid-ence'. When air sinks, it warms up and the amount is given by following down one of the wet adiabats in the tephigram (fig. TR.1) when the sinking air is cloudy. Thus the sinking leads to warming and evaporation which means that cloud in the upper reaches of fronts which are subject to subsidence disappear and leave wide bands of open skies between decks of cloud that is more stubborn than the rest. As the effect occurs from altitude downwards, subsidence can clear upper skies and still leave a mass of thick low cloud near the surface. Sinking air is associated with anticylcones and sometimes with clear skies, but more often than not there is low cloud. In summer this low cloud will burn off with the sun, but at other seasons it may not do so and in winter it produces 'anticyclonic gloom'.

Sometimes in anticyclonic conditions a very strong temperature inversion forms not far from the ground. This subsidence inversion is very difficult to break and usually temperatures rocket while skies produce no cloud. Subsidence inversions inhibit seabreezes and land breezes. See **Inversion**.

Temps is a generic term for all forms of upper-air radiosonde ascents. See **Tephigrams** and **Stüve diagram**.

Tephigrams are thermodynamic diagrams that enable the professional meteorologist to assess cloud height and amount, and what the maximum temperature will be tomorrow, and thus whether there are likely to be showers and/or thunderstorms. They help locate fronts and show the true quality of airmasses which at the surface have been so modified as to be almost unrecognisable. They can show whether air that is not unstable on the lowlands will burst into showers or even storms when forced over a mountain ridge. The information comes by radio telemetry from radiosonde balloons that are released simultaneously at 0000 and 1200 GMT all over the world. The instrument package supplies air pressure, air temperature and wet bulb temperature (see **Hygrometers**), and radar tracking gives the winds at standard pressure levels.

The name of the diagram comes from the major coordinates being temperature (T)

and entropy (φ) hence a tee-phi-gram or tephigram. Entropy is a quantity that stays constant when air cools or warms adiabatically. Thus as this is the way the air acts, the tephigram is directly related to air motion in the vertical. The example (fig. TR.1) shows the major attributes, and the dashed environment curve is plotted from the sonde ascent on a day when thunder developed over south-east England (23 September 1969). The maximum temperature was forecast to get to 26°C (79°F) so air that started as a thermal at A would cool parallel to the dry adiabats until it reached dewpoint temperature of 17°C (63°F) at B. Then it would cool more slowly parallel to the wet adiabats (D, E) and would be down to freezing point at 14 000 ft. (See **Latent heat**.) Above about 21 000 ft it could be cold enough to form the snow that would lead to heavy precipitation, and at 30 000 ft it would stop rising as it reached the same temperature as the environment through which it was rising (F). Thunderstorms or at least heavy showers were inevitable.

To save complication the wet bulb environment curve has not been plotted, but the same remarks apply here as indicated for the **Stüve diagram**. If the two curves are close together, then expect cloud. If they become wide apart, expect open skies.

Thermals are bubbles of air that have been heated to a temperature above that of their surroundings. They lift off and seek cooler realms above, expanding and cooling as they go (fig. TR.2). When they reach dewpoint temperature the moisture they contain condenses into cumulus clouds. Each individual Cu cloud is the visible proof that an invisible thermal source lies below it. Thermal sources are produced by areas which can be heated above their environs – places often quoted are roads, airfield runways, ploughed land, etc. surrounded by woodland, crops or grass.

Fig. TR.1   *A tephigram shows that on this day the air will not stop rising before it reaches 30 000 ft. That must mean thunderstorms. Snow and ice crystals are shown, but not the raindrops and the hailstones that result.*

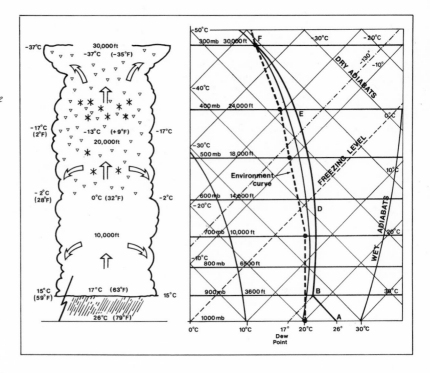

Fig. TR.2   *How thermals lead to cumulus clouds and why the Cu is often not very deep.*

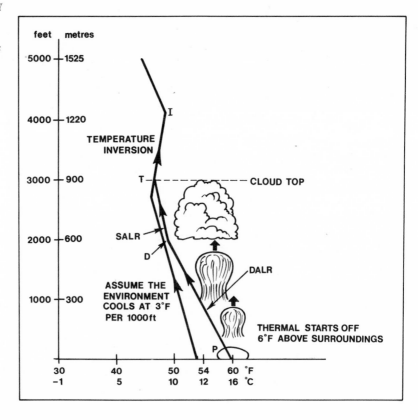

How thermals lead to cumulus clouds is shown in fig. TR.2. The thermal bubble is assumed to start off 6°F (3°C) above its surroundings. The air in the thermal cools at the DALR until it has fallen to dewpoint at D when it cools more slowly at the SALR until it reaches the temperature inversion (I) at 3000 ft (T). The cumulus is therefore 1000 ft deep. We have assumed that the environment cooled at about 3°F per thousand feet of ascent. It can vary very widely.

The production of thermals (as shown by the appearance of Cu) aids the onset of seabreezes and helps them penetrate a long way inland. Inversions militate against thermals, and **subsidence** inversions will inhibit thermals however hot it gets. The much more prevalent overnight **inversion** will be broken in the mornings by thermals punching holes in it. When that happens the wind, previously quiet, wakes up.

Thunderstorms can occur almost anywhere when the conditions are right, and much of what is important to the yachtsman has been covered in chapter 22. Tactical considerations apart, when faced with an advancing storm front that does not appear to have any real breaks in it the only advice is to beat through it as the yacht is too slow to outdistance the normal storm. Monitor its direction of movement from any clouds of the medium levels that may be ahead of it. The storm does not move with the complex wind system it produces at the surface. In particular the heavy gusts at its head come from the left as you face the storm or, put another way, from the storm's viewpoint the gust wind is backed to its direction of movement.

The present weather code for thundery conditions starts with a 9 but is continuous with the mainly showery conditions that are prefixed 8.

90		Moderate or heavy hail shower not associated with thunder
91		Slight rain continuing after a thunderstorm
92		Moderate or heavy rain continuing after a thunderstorm
93		Slight snow, sleet or hail after a thunderstorm
94		As above but moderate or heavy
95		Thunderstorms with rain or snow but no hail – slight or moderate
96		As above but with hail rather than rain or snow
97		Heavy thunderstorm with rain or snow
98		Thunderstorm with dust- or sandstorm
99		Heavy thunderstorm with hail

Tornadoes are localised revolving storms which form over land usually in association with thundery conditions. They may be generated by very active cold fronts, and a succession of many hundreds may be generated, die and be replaced as such a front moves across a land area. Such events have been recorded in central England, but the tornado in Atlantic Europe is not the fatally dangerous beast it is in middle America. The chance of a tornado invading coastal waters is low, but it happens. When over the sea it becomes a tornado storm spout. In sensitive areas the forecasts and advisories will warn of the risks of tornadoes.

Trade winds are so named because of their consistency and speed. They occupy a zone from about 30°N or S towards the equator and tend to migrate with the sun so that sometimes the trades of one hemisphere invade the other. In the NH they are the north-east trades and in the SH the south-east trades. The Atlantic north-east trades blow at an average of about Force 4 (13–15 kn.) and may in places be northerly or easterly.

Tropical revolving storms have been covered under **Cyclones**, but here we can add that they form in the trade-wind belts due to the intensification of weak troughs that invade the low latitudes and move slowly westwards. Such storms do not usually exceed about 150 Nm in diameter, but their central pressure falls to as low as 920 mb with winds that exceed 100 kn. The gusts are much stronger than this.

Tropopause is the top of the atmosphere that is available to weather processes. It can be physically observed when the anvils of big Cb clouds spread out under it (photo C.19). It acts as an impenetrable inversion layer and so prevents further upward convection. More information is to be found in chapter 3.

Troughs may be frontal or non-frontal. Frontal troughs form along fronts and so are recognisable from sky observation, barometric pressure tendencies and weather maps. Non-frontal troughs are more difficult to pin down. They may look like cold fronts as they produce showers very often, but the airmass does not change when they pass (photo C.18). However, pressure falls ahead and rises behind them while winds back ahead (NH) and veer behind. Troughs often follow cold fronts after some hours have passed and they tend to rotate around depression centres like the spokes of a wheel.

Veering and backing The wind is said to veer when it shifts its direction clockwise and to back when it shifts anticlockwise. The term is used in the same sense in both hemispheres. Backing winds are associated with the onset of bad weather but not always, and veering winds are not always associated with better weather.

Visibility is an important aspect of weather when at sea. It is controlled by the amount and nature of the particles in it. In absolutely clean air you can see about 130 Nm, but such a limit is never reached in practice. However, high clouds may be visible for 100 miles sometimes.

In aviation forecasts and coastal station reports, fog means a visibility of less than a kilometre, and mist or haze (smoke) means a visibility of 1–2 km, but in sea area forecasts we have the following: good = more than 5 Nm; moderate = 2–5 Nm; poor = 0.54 Nm (1 km)–2 Nm; fog = less than 0.54 Nm. These limits are too great for vehicle drivers and so the following appear in land area forecasts: mist = 200–1100 yd; fog = less than 200 yd; dense fog = less than 50 yd. See **Fog**, **Mist**, **Station circle**.

Waves are due to the interaction of wind and the water surface. Frictional drag on the water surface causes it to become rhythmically unstable, but once waves grow their very presence induces a degree of turbulence much as if the wind were blowing over a solid surface that had been thrown up into heaps of wave size.

The relationship between the various attributes of waves is as follows (fig. WR.1): speed, C kn. = 3.1 T; length, L m = 1.56 T^2. Thus the longer-period waves travel faster, but not as fast as those of long wavelength. For example, a wave timed to pass a stationary point in 4 s would have a speed of just over 12 kn. and its length would be of the order of 25 m (80 ft). There is no fixed relation between wave height and wave speed, but long waves tend to be low and to travel at very high speed. Thus in detecting the direction

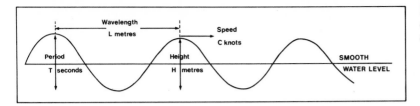

Fig. WR.1 *The terms and symbols used when describing waves.*

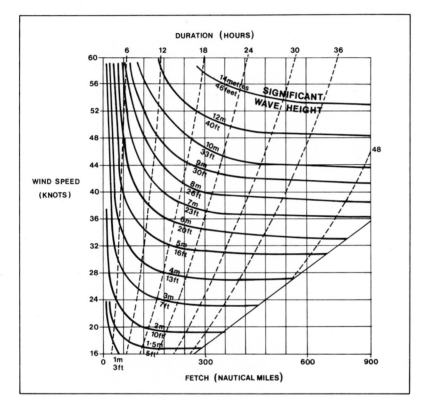

Fig. WR.2 *How to assess significant wave height. (After Dorrestein, Ref. 11.)*

of developing storms a low swell that has run on ahead of the cyclone should be looked for and its direction of travel determined as accurately as possible.

The above only truly applies to waves that are not too large. We have seen in chapter 14 that large waves have both a speed of the wave as a whole plus a speed of the crest which is larger and makes them break in deep water. Waves will naturally break in the shallows as the frictional drag of the bottom retards the base of the wave and the top moves on at the same speed and

falls over the wave front. It is essential in heavy weather to keep well clear of coastal shallows, and attempting to shoot harbour bars is fraught with danger.

The addition of swell to the wave field produces a complex pattern of wave height and period. Swell is waves that have travelled into the area from outside whereas sea waves are those generated by the existing wind. Swell loses half its original height in 1200 Nm of travel, and the group speed of swell waves is only half that of the individual waves themselves.

To the average yachtsman the height to which the waves will grow is the most important criterion and this depends on three factors: wind speed, fetch and duration. In fig. WR.2 these three factors have been plotted against one another in a diagram after Dorrestein. As waves that might be dangerous do not really occur in winds less than Force 4, so the lowest wind speed is 16 kn. and at this speed waves would be 3 ft high after the wind had blown from the same direction for 6 hours. At the other end of the scale an average Force-8 gale (36 kn.) will find the waves 13 ft high after 6 hours, but if you were 60 Nm from the nearest major land mass the waves would not grow larger than this however long the wind blew. Even looking straight out into the ocean wastes and allowing for an exceptional gale that lasted without respite for two days or more, the waves would reach 33 ft and stay there.

That is what research shows happens to actual waves, but chapter 14 shows that other factors lead to rogue waves and sometimes a continuous succession of them.

The wave heights in fig. WR.2 (as in all such diagrams) are 'significant wave heights', which is the average of the highest third of the waves in a train of at least twenty and the waves must be well formed. This indicates the kind of observation the crew at sea must make to establish a wave height that has meaning. However, an estimate of the highest wave to be expected in any 10-minute period can be had by multiplying the value obtained from fig. WR.2 by the following factor:

Wave height factor	1.25	1.35	1.4	1.5	1.6
Duration of storm (hours)	2	6	12	36	infinite

More usefully it has been found that one wave in 23 is twice the average height, but that you have to have 300 000 waves before you find one that is four times the average. Coastal waves tend to be slightly lower than oceanic ones and in either case when the depth is less than half the wavelength the water is shallow enough to cause breaking waves.

REFERENCES

1. *Admiralty List of Radio Signals,* Vol. 3. *Radio Weather Services,* Hydrographer of the Navy.
2. *Admiralty List of Radio Signals,* Vol. 3a. *Weather Reporting and Forecast Areas.*
3. *Admiralty List of Radio Signals,* Vol. 4. *Meteorological Observing Stations.*
4. Bakan, S. An interesting satellite picture, *Weather* June 1983.
5. Browning, K.A. and Harrold, T.W. Air motion and precipitation growth in a wave depression, *Quart. J.R. Met. Soc.* **95**, 288–309.
6. Carlson, T.N. Airflow through mid-latitude cyclones of the comma-cloud pattern, *Amer. Met. Soc. Mon. Wea. Rev.* **108**, 1498–1509.
7. Adlard Coles, K. *Heavy Weather Sailing,* Adlard Coles, 1980.
8. Hamilton, G.D. Buoy capsizing wave conditions, *Log* May–June 1980.
9. Houghton, D. *Weather at Sea,* Royal Yachting Association, 1986.
10. Houghton, D. *Weather Forecasts,* Royal Yachting Association.
11. *Meteorology for Mariners,* HMSO, 1978.
12. Robb, F. *Handling Small Boats in Heavy Weather,* Adlard Coles, 1970.
13. Rousmaniere, J. *Fastnet Force 10,* Nautical Books, 1980.
14. Stephens, O., Kirkman, K. and Peterson, R. Sailing yacht capsizing, *Soc. Nav. Arch. Marine Eng.* 1981.
15. Watts, A. *Cruising Weather,* Nautical Books, 1982.
16. Watts, A. *Dinghy and Board Sailing Weather,* Nautical Books, 1984.
17. Watts, A. The Fastnet factor, *Sail* August 1982.
18. Watts, A. Fresh evidence on the Fastnet storm, *Royal Inst. Navig. J.* **35**(2), 285–92.
19. Watts, A. *Wind and Sailing Boats,* David & Charles, 1987.
20. Watts, A. *Wind Pilot,* Nautical Books, 1975.

INDEX

INDEX

ADDENDUM TO INDEX

Present weather symbols are to be found as
follows (station plot example is on page 191):

*Code
figures*
00–19   phenomena 181
20–29   Past weather 181
30–39   Duststorms etc. (not covered)
40–49   Fog 162
50–59   Drizzle 157
60–69   Rain 187
70–79   Snow 190
80–89   Showers 189
90–99   Thunderstorms 195

In addition see Past weather symbols page 181

Cloud cover in octas 146
High cloud symbols 168
Medium cloud symbols 177
Low cloud symbols 176
Wind arrows 140
Frontogenesis and frontolysis 165
Nephanalysis symbols 179
Occlusion symbols 180
Trough line symbols 167

Beaufort symbols useful for the log are on page
139